SCIENCE:

*CHRISTIAN PERSPECTIVES FOR
THE NEW MILLENNIUM*

SCIENCE:
CHRISTIAN PERSPECTIVES FOR THE NEW MILLENNIUM

Editors:

Scott B. Luley
Paul Copan
Stan W. Wallace

Contributors Include:

Phillip E. Johnson
Henry F. Schaefer III
Alvin Plantinga
Robert Kaita
Walter Bradley
Michael Behe
Wesley Allen

Volume II
Science: Christian Persepctives for the New Millennium

CLM - Christian Leadership Ministries
www.clm.org
P. O. Box 129
Addison, TX 75001-0129
Phone: 972-713-7130 Fax: 972-713-7670
Email: clm@clm.org

RZIM - Ravi Zacharias International Ministries
www.rzim.org
4725 Peachtree Corners Circle Suite 250
Norcross, Georgia, 30092
Phone: 770-449-6766 Fax: 770-729-1729
Email: rzim@rzim.org

Bibliographical references and index
ISBN: 1-930107-20-X
1.Religion and Science 2. Science—Philosophy
3.Naturalism

Printed in the United States of America
Editors: Scott B. Luley, Paul Copan, Stan W. Wallace
First Printing, July 2003
Casebound Edition

SCIENCE:
CHRISTIAN PERSPECTIVES FOR THE NEW MILLENNIUM

Scott B. Luley, Paul Copan, and Stan W. Wallace – Editors
CLM/RZIM Publishers

DEDICATION

—◦◦◦—

*"The philosophy of the classroom in one generation
will be the philosophy of society in the next generation."*

This book project is dedicated to two groups of people seeking to change society in the next generation by influencing the philosophy of the classroom in this generation.

The *first group* includes courageous Christian men and women who seek to integrate their faith and scholarship in the university. As forerunners, these scholars provide articulate "expression" so others can find evidence for a Christian worldview in any discipline.

The *second group* includes the staff of our respective ministries— *Christian Leadership Ministries* (CLM) and *Ravi Zacharias International Ministries* (RZIM). Every person serving with our respective ministries contributed to making this international conference a success.

At the time of the conference, the CLM staff were:

Byron & Dianne Barlowe	*Dr. Walter & Ann Bradley*
Dan & Tricia Clement*	*Jim & Phyllis Cook*
Dr. William Lane & Jan Craig	*Peter & Patti Culver*
Kent & Denise Dahlberg	*Dave & Janet DeHuff*
Paula Dorough	*Mike & Susie Duggins*
Jim & Brenda Dunn	*John & Connie Engberg*
Steve & Wanda Faivre	*Dr. Geri Forsberg & Paul Madison*
Larry & Teresa Freeman*	*Paul & Noelle Gebel*
Dr. Ray & JoAnn Goforth	*Paul & Ethel Gould**
Bill & Jan Hager	*Dr. Pattie Harris*
Paul & Judy Hartgrove	*Don & Linda Hayes**
Gary & Gena Hellman	*Jim Huston*
Mark & Maureen Jacus	*Howie & Nance Kauffman*
Randy & Mary Gayle Kennedy	*Frank & Judy Kifer*

* indicates those who joined CLM staff since the conference.

Ken & Frances Knutzen	Glen & Barbara Leckman
Randy & Cheryl Lee	Dr. Scott & Jan Luley
Phil & Kay Luther	Charlie & Chrissie Mack
John & Sandy Mackin	Dr. Mike & Lisa Madaris
Rich & Bonnie McGee	Dr. Rae & Peggy Mellichamp
Kaye Merritt*	Joe & Jane Mulvihill
John & Cathy Myers	Dr. Dave & Karen Ness
Randy & Pam Newman	Chris & Sharon Peck*
Steve & Sarah Pogue	Dave & Pam Richardson
Patrick & Rachel Rist	Dr. Chuck & Dianne Roeper
Keith & Kay Seabourn	Bob & Jeannette Schroer
Harold & Presha Simmons	Mike & Lee Anne Sorgius
Steve & Betsy Sternberg	Dennis & Norma Suchecki
Dave & Polly Thom	Howard & Debbie Van Cleave
Dr. John & Pat Walkup	Stan & Lori Wallace
Scott & Cathy Waller	Dr. Jim & Anne Wenger
Dave & Beth Wiley	Daryl & Ceil Wilson

At the time of the conference, the RZIM staff were:

Malcolm Armstrong	Scott Armstrong	Helen Barclay
Dolores Barfield	Nancy Bevers	Bonnie Canaday
Merrilee Carlson	Rhonda Caudell	Paul Copan
George Curry	Penny DeHaan	Gavin Douglas
Danielle DuRant	Dan Glaze	Harriett Guinn
Ryan Hayward	Mary Holman	Eric Hunter
Peggy Lasseter	Paul Lundblad	Matt Martz
Bea Maxfield	Mary McAllister	Stuart McAllister
Alistair McPherson	Gordon Moore	Joshua Moore
Travis Poortinga	Laura Reinert	Andy Rhodes
Erik Rowe	Kara Sanford	Becky Schulz
Bill Smith	Steve Unwin	Mark Veerman
Linda Wolfe	Margie Zacharias	Naomi Zacharias
Nathan Zacharias	Ravi Zacharias	

CLM, the faculty ministry of Campus Crusade for Christ, reaches out to and through professors and future professors at secular universities to *win* them to faith in Jesus Christ, *build* them in their faith, and *send* them to influence others on campuses in the United States and around the world.

RZIM seeks to reach and challenge those who shape the ideas of culture with the credibility and the beauty of the Gospel of Jesus Christ through evangelism, apologetics, spiritual disciplines, and training.

ACKNOWLEDGMENTS

—⚜—

It has been a pleasure for us to work together on this multi-book project. Our partnership began as we served together on the Program Committee for the *God and the Academy Conference*, which was co-hosted by our ministries (CLM and RZIM).

We acknowledge all who designed and implemented the *God and the Academy Conference* which this book documents. It was a team effort by both ministries.

Special thanks to several people who contributed significantly to this book series. Deirdre Boyer and Steve Hollaway helped in many different ways throughout the publishing process. Ryan Bonfiglio, a Princeton University graduate, gave valuable feedback on how each volume's essays could best reach the target audience we chose. Alison Lentini and Tricia Clement gave editorial advice and LeeAnne Sorgius, Anna McCarroll, and Deirdre Boyer transcribed many audiotapes of the conference lectures into manuscripts for editing.

We acknowledge the founding members of CLM's Academic Initiative Executive Committee—Bob Schroer, Patrick Rist, Randy Newman and Scott Waller—for their help in planning and helping direct the *God and the Academy Conference* program. These men are exemplars of scholar-activists who deeply love both Christ and the academy.

We acknowledge the contributions of three RZIM staff—Gordon Moore, Sarah Davis, and Joshua Moore, all who accepted the task of formatting the volumes in our series. Sarah Davis joined RZIM after the conference, but gave valuable input and support to this co-publishing venture of CLM and RZIM.

Projects of this magnitude always require the support of family and co-workers. We acknowledge their commitment to Jesus Christ and His desire to "seek and speak" to those for whom this book is written.

SCOTT B. LULEY, PH.D.

Director, Christian Leadership Ministries at Princeton University
& the Eastern US Region

 Scott Luley earned his B.S. degree from Lehigh University and his M.B.A. and Ph.D. degrees from Penn State University. In 1980 he helped to found Christian Leadership Ministries. Dr. Luley is currently Director of Christian Leadership Ministries at Princeton University and in the Eastern US Region. He lives near Princeton University with his wife Jan and two teenage boys.

PAUL COPAN, PH.D.

Lecturer and Author, Ravi Zacharias International Ministries and
Visiting Associate Professor, Trinity International University

 Paul Copan has studied at Columbia Bible College (B.A.), Trinity Evangelical Divinity School (M.A., Philosophy of Religion; M.Div.), and Marquette University (Milwaukee), where he received his Ph.D. in philosophy. He is a Visiting Assistant Professor at Trinity Evangelical Divinity School. He has co-authored and written several books and is currently ministry associate with RZIM. He currently resides in Suwanee, GA with his wife Jacqueline and their five children.

STAN W. WALLACE, M.A.

Coordinator, Emerging Scholars Network and Gulf States Area Director
InterVarsity Christian Fellowship Graduate and Faculty Ministries

 Stan Wallace earned his B.S. in Education from Miami University, his M.A. in Philosophy of Religion and Ethics from Talbot School of Theology, and has pursued doctoral studies in Philosophy at Marquette University. He is currently Coordinator of the Emerging Scholars Network and serves as an Area Director with Intervarsity Christian Fellowship's Graduate and Faculty Ministries. Stan lives in Tampa, Florida with his wife Lori and four children.

INTRODUCTION

—◦/◦/◦—

We live in an era called "postmodern." Today, the term is overused, but it accurately describes the skeptical responses and rejection of objective truth claims—especially those proposing answers to life's most important and ultimate questions. Today, many "modernist" systems (Enlightenment rationalism, Marxism, and/or Nazism) have failed to deliver their utopian promises, leaving many to wonder if all that is left are the idiosyncratic beliefs of individuals and social groups. We are told this is the postmodern mindset.

One pervasive and influential worldview in our contemporary culture seeking to offer a comprehensive explanation of the way things are is scientific naturalism. It claims all that exists and can be experienced must be explained only in terms of natural, as opposed to supernatural, causes.

Our current culture provides a mixed bag of approaches to truth, knowledge, life, meaning, and purpose. Christians in any sector of society are confronted by challenges to the Gospel and revelation—in any form— by skeptics of truth claims as they are urged to adopt a secular worldview.

To deal with challenges like these, Ravi Zacharias International Ministries and Christian Leadership Ministries partnered together to sponsor *God and the Academy: Charting a Course for the New Millennium*. This was a conference international in scope and designed to bring together Christians who recognize the "culture-shaping" influence of education—particularly in the secular university. The conference was held at the Georgia Institute of Technology in June 2000.

Charles Malik, former President of the United Nations General Assembly, proposed "two tasks" for higher education—one spiritual and the other intellectual, saving the soul and saving the mind.

> All the preaching in the world, and all the loving care
> of even the best parents between whom there are no
> problems whatever, will amount to little, if not to
> nothing, so long as what the children are exposed to
> day in and day out for fifteen to twenty years in the
> school and university virtually cancels out, morally and
> spiritually, what they hear and see and learn at home
> and in the church.[1]

As Christians, we are called to evangelism, but also to engage education in a dialogue that challenges the reigning assumptions and ideas underlying our postmodern culture.

In 1913, the President of Princeton Theological Seminary, J. Gresham Machen, expressed this same vision with words that ring as true today as they did then:

> We may preach with all the fervor of a reformer and
> yet succeed only in winning a straggler here and there,
> if we permit the whole collective thought of the
> nation to be controlled by ideas that, by the resistless
> force of logic, prevent Christianity from being regarded
> as anything more than a harmless delusion.[2]

To this end, we offer the following volumes to "capture" the ideas proposed and discussed at the conference our ministries co-sponsored: Philosophy: Christian Perspectives for the New Millennium and Science: Christian Perspectives for the New Millennium.

These volumes are designed to: (1) help believers think Christianly about a wide array of topics, and (2) offer ideas and dialogue to those outside the Christian community who often have legitimate questions about the Gospel. We feel there is more than enough evidence to challenge any serious skeptic who understands that God never minds serious questions—only the insult of being ignored.

Jeremiah wrote in the Old Testament,

> Thus says the Lord, "Let not a wise man boast of his
> wisdom, and let not the mighty man boast of his

might, let not a rich man boast of his riches; but let him who boasts boast of this, that he understands and knows Me, that I am the Lord who exercises lovingkindness, justice, and righteousness on earth; for I delight in these things," declares the Lord.[3]

As co-editors, we are committed to the integration of faith and learning in education. Our lives, ministries, and these volumes reflect a commitment to advance the cause of Christ by presenting a Christian worldview in secular universities. That viewpoint is often marginalized in the university community. To address this situation, great effort has been exerted to design this book to reflect the issues thinking Christians everywhere often discuss. As editors, we have done this in several ways.

First, we chose *authors* who are currently some of the best thinkers within the Christian community—most are professors at prominent secular universities. Second, we chose *topics* that are at the center of debate in secular universities and society in general. Third, we included "give and take" audience *discussions* from the same or a similar lecture given at a prominent secular university. These lectures and audience discussions are very helpful as they reveal what many students today think, feel, and believe. We are committed to the inclusion of such material, as it can prevent our "talking to ourselves." These volumes reflect a sincere attempt to engage the academy and culture of our time.

This science volume focuses on two of the most passionately debated issues in science today – Naturalism and Intelligent Design.

The volume is divided into four parts. Each author is a world-class scholar who has taken debatable issues in science to popular places in the academy and society in general.

Part I offers several Christian perspectives on philosophy in science.

Berkeley Law Professor *Phillip Johnson* ("What is Darwinism?") dissects, in a masterful, yet understandable, way the pervasive influence Darwinism has in science. He discusses the underlying questions about

Darwinism and why its advocates tend to not be receptive to its critics—especially those in the community of faith. Computational Quantum Chemist *Henry F. Schaefer* ("The Big Bang, Stephen Hawking, and God") blends the literature he cites and his professional experience in science to help us understand why science promotes naturalism.

Part II offers several Christian perspectives on naturalism in science.

In his second essay, *Phillip Johnson* ("Is Scientific Naturalism Scientific? with Audience Discussion") exposes how scientific naturalism affects the field of science today. The audience discussion section of *Johnson's* essay allows readers to benefit from the dialogue after the same lecture given at another time at Princeton University. Philosopher, *Alvin Plantinga* ("Should Methodological Naturalism Constrain Science?") makes a masterful case for pursuing science with all we know as Christians. When objectively examined on this basis, Plantinga believes naturalism, although widely accepted, offers weak arguments that should be rejected.

Part III offers several Christian perspectives on intelligent design in science.

Physicist *Robert Kaita* ("Does our Universe Reveal a Designer, Creator, or Nothing at All?") explains why he believes we live in a "caused" universe and why science becomes a rational thing to do only in a "created and caused universe." Professor and popular university speaker *Walter Bradley* ("Does Recent Scientific Evidence Support a Designed Universe? with Audience Discussion") uses physics, chemistry, and thermodynamics to demonstrate the precise design our universe exhibits and the implications of that fact on the question of whether it was designed or not. The audience discussion section of *Bradley's* essay captures dialogue between Professor Bradley and an audience at Princeton University. Biochemist *Michael Behe* ("The Modern Intelligent Design hypothesis: Breaking the Rules") contrasts the modern view of intelligent design with older versions, showing the former to offer a conclusion of design using scientific evidence rather than theological or philosophical claims that God is the designer. The criticisms of several scientific opponents of design, including Kenneth R. Miller's book, *Finding Darwin's God*[4], are examined and found to support, rather than deny, the case for design in the universe.

Part IV offers a Christian scientist's perspective on the future of science.

Quantum Chemist *Wesley Allen* ("Modern Science: Charting a Course for the Future") proposes four principles he feels are necessary to safeguard scientific discourse in the future. He articulates the "tension" between our Christian heritage and methodological naturalism, the pervasive worldview in science today. Dr. Allen makes a case for Christian scholarship being shaped by the Christian worldview as we start the 21st Century.

We hope the essays in this volume on science—along with its companion volume on philosophy—will stimulate you to think further about these important issues as you read some of the greatest Christian thinkers in the world. As co-editors, the three of us are committed to this goal.

Scott B. Luley, Ph.D.
>   *Director, Christian Leadership Ministries at Princeton University*
>   *& the Eastern US Region*

Paul Copan, Ph.D.
>   *Lecturer, Ravi Zacharias International Ministries and*
>   *Visiting Associate Professor at Trinity International University*

Stan W. Wallace, M.A.
>   *Coordinator, Emerging Scholars Network and Gulf States Area Director*
>   *InterVarsity Christian Fellowship Graduate and Faculty Ministries*

---

1 Charles Malik, The Two Tasks (Westchester, Ill.: Crossway, 1980): 27.

2 "Christianity and Culture," *Princeton Theological Review* 11 (1913): 7.

3 Jeremiah 9:23-24.

4 Miller, Kenneth R. *Finding Darwin's God* (New York: Harper Collins Publishers, 1999).

PART I:

PHILOSOPHY IN SCIENCE

Chapter One

WHAT IS DARWINISM?[1]

Phillip Johnson

Phillip Johnson is the Jefferson E. Peyser Professor of Law, Emeritus at the University of California at Berkeley and has been on the law faculty there since 1968. He authored two law school casebooks and wrote several best-selling books on science, philosophy and religion, including Darwin on Trial, Reason in the Balance: The Case Against Naturalism in Science, Law, and Education, and The Right Questions: Truth, Meaning, and Public Debate. Professor Johnson also served as Associate Dean at UC, Berkeley for three years and has expertise on a wide variety of law subjects, including criminal law, criminal procedure, and contemporary legal theory and has served as a law clerk in both the California Supreme Court and the U.S. Supreme Court.

Abstract

As many philosophers of science have observed, the research community does not abandon a paradigm in the absence of a suitable replacement. This means that negative criticism of Darwinism, however devastating it may appear to be, is essentially irrelevant to the professional researchers. The critic may point out, for example, that evidence that natural selection has any creative power is somewhere between weak and non-existent. That is perfectly true, but to Darwinists the more important point is this: If natural selection did not do the creating, what did? 'God' is obviously unacceptable, because such a being is unknown to science. "We don't know" is equally unacceptable because admitting ignorance would leave science adrift without a guiding principle

THERE IS A POPULAR TELEVISION GAME SHOW called "Jeopardy," in which the usual order of things is reversed. Instead of being asked a question to which they must supply the answer, the contestants are given the answer and asked to provide the appropriate question. This format suggests an insight that is applicable to law, to science, and indeed to just about everything. The important thing is not necessarily to know all the answers, but rather to know what question is being asked.

That insight is the starting point for my inquiry into Darwinian evolution and its relationship to creation because Darwinism is the answer to two very different kinds of questions. First, Darwinian theory tells us how a certain amount of diversity in life forms can develop once we have various types of complex living organisms already in existence. If a small population of birds happens to migrate to an isolated island, for example, a combination of inbreeding, mutation, and natural selection may cause this isolated population to develop different characteristics from those possessed by the ancestral population on the mainland. When the theory is understood in this limited sense, Darwinian evolution is uncontroversial, and has no important philosophical or theological implications.

Evolutionary biologists are not content merely to explain how variation occurs within limits, however. They aspire to answer a much broader question — which is how complex organisms like birds, and flowers, and human beings came into existence in the first place. The Darwinian answer to this second question is that the creative force that produced complex plants and animals from single-celled predecessors over long stretches of geological time is essentially the same as the mechanism that produces variations in flowers, insects, and domestic animals before our very eyes. In the words of Ernst Mayr, the dean of living Darwinists, "trans-specific evolution [i.e., macroevolution] is nothing but an extrapolation and magnification of the events that take place within populations and species."

Neo-Darwinian evolution in this broad sense is a philosophical doctrine so lacking in empirical support that Mayr's successor at Harvard, Stephen Jay Gould, once pronounced it, in a reckless moment, to be "effectively dead."[2] Yet neo-Darwinism is far from dead; on the contrary, it is continually proclaimed in the textbooks and the media as unchallengeable fact. How does it happen that so many scientists and intellectuals, who pride themselves on their empiricism and open-mindedness, continue to accept an unempirical theory as scientific fact?

Neo-Darwinian evolution in this broad sense is a philosophical doctrine so lacking in empirical support that Mayr's successor at Harvard, Stephen Jay Gould, once pronounced it, in a reckless moment, to be "effectively dead."

The answer to that question lies in the definition of five key terms. The terms are *creationism, evolution, science, religion,* and *truth*. Once we understand how these words are used in evolutionary discourse, the continued ascendancy of neo-Darwinism will be no mystery and we need no longer be deceived by claims that the theory is supported by "overwhelming evidence."

I should warn at the outset, however, that using words clearly is not the innocent and peaceful activity most of us may have thought it to be. There are powerful vested interests in this area that can thrive only in the midst of ambiguity and confusion. Those who insist on defining terms precisely and using them consistently may find themselves regarded with suspicion and hostility, and even accused of being enemies of science. But let us accept that risk and proceed to the definitions.

Creation and Creationism

The first word is *creationism*, which means simply a belief in creation. In Darwinist usage, which dominates not only the popular and profession scientific literature but also the media, a creationist is a person who takes the creation account in the book of Genesis to be true in a very literal sense. The earth was created in a single week of six 24-hour days no more that 10,000 years ago; the major features of the geological record were produced by Noah's flood; and there have been no major innovations in the forms of life since the beginning. It is a major theme of Darwinist propaganda that the only persons who have any doubts about Darwinism are young-earth creationists of this sort, who are always portrayed as rejecting the clear and convincing evidence of science to preserve a religious prejudice. The implication is that citizens of modern society are faced with a choice that is really no choice at all. Either they reject science altogether and retreat to a pre-modern worldview, or they believe everything the Darwinists tell them.

In a broader sense, however, a creationist is simply a person who believes in the existence of a creator, who brought about the existence of the world and its living inhabitants in furtherance of a purpose.

In a broader sense, however, a creationist is simply a person who believes in the existence of a *creator*, who brought about the existence of the world and its living inhabitants in furtherance of a *purpose*. Whether the process of creation took a single week or billions of years is relatively unimportant from a philosophical or theological standpoint. Creation by gradual processes over geological ages may create problems for biblical interpretation, but it creates none for the basic principle of theistic religion. And creation in this broad sense, according to a 1991 Gallup poll, is the creed of 87 percent of Americans. If God brought about our existence for a purpose, then the most important kind of knowledge to have is knowledge of God and of what He intends for us. Is creation in that broad sense consistent with evolution?

Evolution and Naturalism

The answer is absolutely not, when "evolution" is understood in the Darwinian sense. To Darwinists, evolution means *naturalistic* evolution, because they insist that science must assume that the cosmos is a closed system of material causes and effects, which can never be influenced by anything outside of material nature—by God, for example. In the beginning, an undirected explosion of matter created the cosmos, and undirected, naturalistic evolution produced everything that followed. From this philosophical standpoint it follows deductively that from the beginning no intelligent purpose guided evolution. If intelligence exists today, that is only because it has itself evolved through purposeless material processes.

That such complex entities came into existence simply by chance is clearly less credible than that they were designed and constructed by a creator. To back up their claim that this appearance of intelligent design is an illusion, Darwinists need to provide some complexity-building force that is mindless and purposeless. Natural selection is by far the most plausible candidate.

A materialistic theory of evolution must inherently invoke two kinds of processes. At bottom, the theory must be based on chance because that is what is left when we have ruled out everything involving intelligence or purpose. Theories that invoke *only* chance, though, are not credible, however. One thing everyone acknowledges is that living organisms are enormously complex—far more so than, say, a computer or an airplane. That such complex entities came into existence simply by chance is clearly less credible than that they were designed and constructed by a creator. To back up their claim that this appearance of intelligent design is an illusion, Darwinists need to provide some complexity-building force that is mindless and purposeless. Natural selection is by far the most plausible candidate.

If we assume that random genetic mutations provided the new genetic information needed, say, to give a small mammal a start towards wings, and if we assume that each tiny step in the process of wing-building gave the animal an increased chance of survival, then natural selection ensured that the favored creatures would thrive and reproduce. It follows as a matter of logic that wings can and will appear as if by the plan of a designer. Of course, if wings or other improvements do not appear, the theory explains their absence just as well. The needed mutations didn't arrive, or "developmental constraints" closed off certain possibilities, or natural selection favored something else. There is no requirement that any of this speculation be confirmed by either experimental or fossil evidence. To Darwinists, just being able to imagine the process is sufficient to confirm that something like that must have happened.

Richard Dawkins calls the process of creation by mutation and selection "the blind watchmaker." By using this label, he means that a purposeless, materialistic designing force substitutes for the "watchmaker" deity of natural theology. The creative power of the blind watchmaker is supported only by very slight evidence, such as the famous example of a moth population in which the percentage of dark moths increased during a period when the birds were better able to see light moths against the smoke-darkened background trees. This may be taken to show that natural selection can do something, but not that it can create anything that was not already in existence. Even such slight evidence is more than sufficient, however, because evidence is not really necessary to prove something that is practically self-evident. The existence of a potent blind watchmaker follows deductively from the philosophical premise that nature had to do its own creating. There can be argument about the details, but if God was not in the picture something very much like Darwinism simply has to be true, regardless of the evidence.

Science and Its Paradigms

That brings me to my third term, *science*. We have already seen that Darwinists assume as a matter of first principle that the history of the cosmos and its life forms is fully explicable on naturalistic principles. This reflects a philosophical doctrine called scientific naturalism, which is said to be a necessary consequence of the inherent limitations of science. What scientific naturalism does, however, is to transform the limitations of science into limitations upon reality, in the interest of maximizing the explanatory power of science and its practitioners. It is, of course, entirely possible to study organisms scientifically on the premise that they were all created by God, just as scientists study airplanes and even works of art without denying that these objects are intelligently designed. The problem with allowing God a role in the history of life is not that science would cease, but rather that scientists would have to acknowledge the existence of something important which is outside the boundaries of natural science. For scientists who want to be able to explain everything—and "theories of everything" are now openly anticipated in the scientific literature—this is an intolerable possibility.

The problem with allowing God a role in the history of life is not that science would cease, but rather that scientists would have to acknowledge the existence of something important which is outside the boundaries of natural science.

The second feature of scientific naturalism that is important for our purpose is its set of rules governing the criticism and replacement of a paradigm. A paradigm is a general theory, like the Darwinian theory of evolution, which has achieved general acceptance in the scientific community. The paradigm unifies the various specialties that make up the research community, and guides research in all of them. Thus, zoologists, botanists, geneticists, molecular biologists, and paleontologists all see their research as aimed at filling out the details of the Darwinian paradigm. If molecular biologists see a pattern of apparently neutral mutations, which have no apparent effect on an organism's fitness, they must find a way to reconcile their findings with the paradigm's requirement that natural selection guides evolution. This they do by postulating a sufficient quantity of invisible adaptive mutations, which are deemed to be accumulated by natural selection. Similarly, if paleontologists see new fossil species appearing suddenly in the fossil record, and remaining basically unchanged thereafter, they must perform whatever contortions are necessary to force this recalcitrant evidence into a model of incremental change through the accumulation of micromutations.

Supporting the paradigm may even require what in other contexts would be called deception. As Niles Eldredge candidly admitted, "We paleontologists have said that the history of life supports [the story of gradual adaptive change], all the while knowing it does not."[3] Eldredge explained that this pattern of misrepresentation occurred because of "the certainty so characteristic of evolutionary ranks since the late 1940s, the utter assurance not only that natural selection operates in nature, but that we know precisely how it works." This certainty produced a degree of dogmatism that Eldredge says resulted in the relegation to the "lunatic fringe" of paleontologists who reported, "they saw something out of kilter between contemporary evolutionary theory, on the one hand, and patterns of change in the fossil record on the other."[4] Under the circumstances, prudent paleontologists understandably swallowed their doubts and supported the ruling ideology. To abandon the paradigm would be to abandon the scientific community; to ignore the paradigm and just gather the facts would be to earn the demeaning label of "stamp collector."

As many philosophers of science have observed, the research community does not abandon a paradigm in the absence of a suitable replacement. This means that negative criticism of Darwinism, however devastating it may appear to be, is essentially irrelevant to the professional researchers. The critic may point out, for example, that the evidence that natural selection has any creative power is somewhere between weak and non-existent. That is perfectly true, but to Darwinists the more important point is this: If natural selection did not do the creating, what did? "God" is obviously unacceptable, because such a being is unknown to science. "We don't know" is equally unacceptable, because to admit ignorance would be to leave science adrift without a guiding principle. To put the problem in the most practical terms: it is impossible to write or evaluate a grant proposal without a generally accepted theoretical framework.

... the evidence that natural selection has any creative power is somewhere between weak and non-existent.

The paradigm rule explains why Gould's acknowledgment that neo-Darwinism is "effectively dead" had no significant effect on the Darwinist faithful, or even on Gould himself. Gould made that statement in a paper predicting the emergence of a new general theory of evolution, one based on the macromutational speculations of the Berkeley geneticist Richard Goldschmidt.[5] When the new theory did not arrive as anticipated, the alternatives were either to stick with Ernst

Mayr's version of neo-Darwinism, or to concede that biologists do not after all know of a naturalistic mechanism that can produce biological complexity. That was no choice at all. Gould had to beat a hasty retreat back to classical Darwinism to avoid giving aid and comfort to the enemies of scientific naturalism, including those disgusting creationists.

Having to defend a dead theory tooth and nail can hardly be a satisfying activity, and it is no wonder that Gould lashes out with fury at people such as myself, who call attention to his predicament.[6] I do not mean to ridicule Gould because I have a genuinely high regard for the man. He is one of the few Darwinists who has recognized the major problems with the theory and reported them honestly. His tragedy is that he cannot admit the clear implications of his own thought without effectively resigning from science.

The continuing survival of Darwinist orthodoxy illustrates Thomas Kuhn's famous point that the accumulation of anomalies never in itself falsifies a paradigm, because "To reject one paradigm without substituting another is to reject science itself."[7] This practice may be appropriate as a way of carrying on the professional enterprise called science, but it can be grossly misleading when it is imposed upon persons who are asking questions other than the ones scientific naturalists want to ask. Suppose, for example, that I want to know whether God really had something to do with creating living organisms. A typical Darwinian response is that there is no reason to invoke supernatural action because Darwinian selection was capable of performing the job. To evaluate that response, I need to know whether natural selection really has the fantastic creative power attributed to it. It is not a sufficient answer to say that scientists have nothing better to offer. The fact that scientists don't like to say "we don't know" tells me nothing about what they really *do* know.

I am not suggesting that scientists have to change their rules about retaining and discarding paradigms. All I want them to do is to be candid about the disconfirming evidence and admit, if it is the case, that they are hanging on to Darwinism only because they prefer a shaky theory to having no theory at all. What they insist upon doing, however, is to present Darwinian evolution to the public as a fact that every rational person is expected to accept. If there are reasonable grounds to doubt the theory such dogmatism is ridiculous, whether or not the doubters have a better theory to propose.

Religion and Reason

To believers in creation, the Darwinists seem thoroughly intolerant and dogmatic when they insist that their own philosophy must have a monopoly in the schools and the media. The Darwinists do not see themselves that way, of course. On the contrary, they often feel aggrieved when creationists (in either the broad or narrow sense) ask to have their own arguments heard in public and fairly considered. To insist that schoolchildren be taught that Darwinian evolution as a fact is, in their minds, merely to protect the integrity of science education; to present the other side of the case would be to allow fanatics to force their opinions on others. Even college professors have been forbidden to express their doubts about Darwinian evolution in the classroom, and it seems to be widely believed that the Constitution not only permits, but actually requires, such restrictions on academic freedom. To explain this bizarre situation, we must define our fourth term: *religion*.

Suppose a skeptic argues that evidence for biological creation by natural selection is obviously lacking, and, under the circumstances, we ought to give serious consideration to the possibility that the development of life required some input from a pre-existing, purposeful creator. To scientific naturalists, this suggestion is "creationist" and therefore unacceptable in principle, because it invokes an entity unknown to science. What is worse, it suggests the possibility that this creator may have communicated in some way with humans. In that case, there could be real prophets – persons with a genuine knowledge of God who are neither frauds nor dreamers. Such persons could conceivably be dangerous rivals for the scientists as cultural authorities.

The strategy naturalistic philosophy uses to prevent this problem from arising is to label naturalism as science and theism as religion. The former is then classified as *knowledge*, and the latter as mere *belief*. The distinction is of critical importance, because only knowledge can be objectively valid for everyone; belief is valid only for the believer, and should never be passed off as knowledge. The student who thinks that 2 plus 2 equals 5, or that water is not made up of hydrogen and oxygen, or that the theory of evolution is not true, is not expressing a minority viewpoint. He or she is ignorant, and the job of education is to cure that ignorance and to replace it with knowledge. Students in the public schools are thus to be taught at an early age that "evolution is a fact," and as time goes by they will gradually learn that evolution means naturalism.

The strategy naturalistic philosophy uses to prevent this problem from arising is to label naturalism as science and theism as religion. The former is then classified as "knowledge," and the latter as "mere belief."

In short, the proposition that God was in any way involved in our creation is effectively outlawed, and implicitly negated. This is because naturalistic evolution is by definition in the category of scientific knowledge. What contradicts knowledge is implicitly false, or imaginary. That is why it is possible for scientific naturalists in good faith to claim that their science says nothing about God, yet, to claim on the other hand that they have said everything that can be said about God. In naturalistic philosophy, both propositions are at bottom the same. All that needs to be said about God is that there is nothing to be said of God, because on that subject we can have no knowledge.

Truth

Our fifth and final term is *truth*. Truth as such is not a particularly important concept in naturalistic philosophy. The reason for this is that "truth" suggests an unchanging absolute, whereas scientific knowledge is a dynamic concept. Like life, knowledge evolves and grows into superior forms. What was knowledge in the past is not knowledge today, and the knowledge of the future will surely be far superior to what we have now. Only naturalism itself and the unique validity of science as the path to knowledge are absolutes. There can be no criterion for truth outside of scientific knowledge, no mind of God to which we have access.

This way of understanding things persists even when scientific naturalists employ religious-sounding language. For example, the physicist Stephen Hawking ended his famous book *A Brief History of Time*[8] with the prediction that man might one day "know the mind of God." This phrasing causes some to form the mistaken impression that he had some attraction to theistic religion. In context, Hawking was not referring to a supernatural eternal being, but to the possibility that scientific knowledge will eventually become complete and all-encompassing because it will have explained the movements of material particles in all circumstances.

The monopoly of science in the realm of knowledge explains why evolutionary biologists do not find it meaningful to address the question of whether the Darwinian theory is true. They will gladly concede that the theory is incomplete, and that further research into the mechanisms of evolution is needed. At any given point in time, however, the reigning theory of naturalistic evolution represents the state of scientific knowledge about how we came into existence. Scientific knowledge is by definition the closest approximation of absolute truth available to us. To ask whether this knowledge is true is therefore to miss the point, and to betray a misunderstanding of "how science works."

So far, I have described the metaphysical categories by which scientific naturalists have excluded the topic of God from rational discussion, and thus ensured that Darwinism's fully naturalistic creation story is effectively true by definition. There is no need to explain why atheists find this system of thought control congenial. What is a little more difficult to understand, at least at first, is the strong support Darwinism continues to receive in the Christian academic world. Attempts to investigate the credibility of the Darwinist evolution story are regarded with little enthusiasm by many leading Christian professors of science and philosophy, even at institutions that are generally regarded as conservative in theology.

Given that Darwinism is inherently naturalistic, and therefore antagonistic to the idea that God had anything to do with the history of life, and that it plays the central role in ensuring agnostic domination of the intellectual culture, one might suppose that Christian intellectuals and religious Jews would be eager to find its weak spots. Instead, the prevailing view among Christian professors has been that Darwinism— or "evolution," as they tend to call it — is unbeatable, and that it can be interpreted to be consistent with Christian belief.

Theistic Evolution

In fact, Darwinism is unbeatable as long as one accepts the thought categories of scientific naturalism I have been describing. The problem is that those same thought categories make Christian theism, or any other theism, absolutely untenable. If science has exclusive authority to tell us how life was created, and if science is committed to naturalism, and if science never discards a paradigm until it is presented with an acceptable naturalistic alternative, then Darwinism's position is impregnable within science. The same reasoning that makes Darwinism inevitable, however, also bans God from taking any action within the history of the Cosmos, which means that it makes theism illusory. Theistic naturalism is self-contradictory.

The same reasoning that makes Darwinism inevitable, however, also bans God from taking any action within the history of the Cosmos, which means that it makes theism illusory. Theistic naturalism is self-contradictory.

Some hope to avoid the contradiction by asserting that naturalism rules only within the realm of science, and that there is a separate realm called "religion" in which theism can flourish. The problem with this arrangement, as we have already seen, is that in a naturalistic culture scientific conclusions are considered to be knowledge, or even fact. What is outside of fact is fantasy, or at best subjective belief. Theists who accommodate with scientific naturalism therefore may never affirm that their God is *real* in the same sense that evolution is real. This rule is essential to the entire mindset that produced Darwinism in the first place. If God exists He could certainly work through mutation and selection if that is what He wanted to do, but He could also create by some means totally outside the ken of our science.

Once we put God into the picture, there is no good reason to attribute the creation of biological complexity to random mutation and natural selection. Direct evidence that these mechanisms have substantial creative power is not to be found in nature, the laboratory, or the fossil record. An essential step in the reasoning that establishes that Darwinian selection created the wonders of biology, therefore, is that nothing else *was* available. Theism is by definition the doctrine that something else was available.

Perhaps the contradiction is hard to see when it is stated at an abstract level; so I will give a more concrete example. Persons who advocate the compromise position called "theistic evolution" are, in my experience, always vague about what they mean by "evolution." They have good reason to be vague. As we have seen, Darwinian evolution is by definition unguided and purposeless, and such evolution cannot in any meaningful sense be theistic. For evolution to be genuinely theistic, it must be guided by God, whether this means that God programmed the process in advance or stepped in from time to time to give it a push in the right direction. To Darwinists evolution guided by God is a soft form of creationism, which is to say it is not evolution at all. To repeat, this understanding goes to the very heart of Darwinist thinking. Allow a preexisting supernatural intelligence to guide evolution, and this omnipotent being can do a whole lot more than that.

Of course, theists can think of evolution as God-guided whether naturalistic Darwinists like it or not. The trouble with having a private definition for theists, however, is that the scientific naturalists have the power to decide what that term "evolution" means in public discourse, including the science classes in the public schools. If theistic evolutionists broadcast the message that evolution as *they* understand it is harmless to theistic religion, they are misleading their constituents unless they add a clear warning that the version of evolution advocated by the entire body of mainstream science is something else altogether. That warning is never clearly delivered, however, because the main point of theistic evolution is to preserve peace with the mainstream scientific community. The theistic evolutionists therefore unwitting serve the purposes of the scientific naturalists, by helping persuade the religious community to lower its guard against the incursion of naturalism's chosen method of creation.

What is Darwinism?

We are now in a position to answer the question with which we began. What is Darwinism? Darwinism is a theory of empirical science only at the level of microevolution, where it provides a framework for explaining such things as the diversity that arises when small populations become reproductively isolated from the main body of the species. As a general theory of biological creation, Darwinism is not empirical at all. Rather, it is a necessary implication of a philosophical doctrine called scientific naturalism, which is based on the *a priori* assumption that God was always absent from the realm of nature. As such, evolution in the Darwinian sense is inherently antithetical to theism, although evolution in some entirely different and non-naturalistic sense could conceivably have been God's chosen method of creation.

As a general theory of biological creation, Darwinism is not empirical at all. Rather, it is a necessary implication of a philosophical doctrine called scientific naturalism ....

In 1874, the great Presbyterian theologian Charles Hodge asked the question I have asked: "What is Darwinism?" After a careful and thoroughly fair-minded evaluation of the doctrine, his answer was unequivocal: "It is Atheism." Another way to state the proposition is to say that Darwinism is the answer to a specific question that grows out of philosophical naturalism. To return to the game of "Jeopardy" with which we started, let us say that Darwinism is the answer. What, then, is the question? The question is: "How must creation have occurred if we assume that God had nothing to do with it?"

Instead, we need to challenge the assumption that the only questions worth asking are ones that assume that naturalism is true.

Theistic evolutionists accomplish very little by trying to Christianize the answer to a question that comes straight out of the agenda of scientific naturalism. Instead, we need to challenge the assumption that the only questions worth asking are ones that assume that naturalism is true.

[1] This essay was taken from *Objections Sustained: Subversive Essays on Evolution, Law & Culture* by Phillip E. Johnson. Copyright (c) 1998 by Phillip E. Johnson. It is used by permission of InterVarsity Press, P.O. Box 1400, Downers Grove, IL 60515 (www.ivpress.com).

[2] Gould, Stephen Jay. "Is a New and General Theory of Evolution Emerging?" Paleobiology. 6 (1980): 119-130, reprinted in Maynard Smith, ed., *Evolution Now: A Century After Darwin* (New York: W. H. Freeman, 1982).

[3] Eldredge, Niles. *Time Frames* (Portsmouth, N.H.H: Heinemann, 1986 or New York: Simon & Schuster, New York: Simon & Schuster, 1986): 144.

[4] Ibid., 93.

[5] Gould, 119-130.

[6] See Stephen Jay Gould, "Impeaching a Self-Appointed Judge," *Scientific American.*, (July 1992): 118-122. *Scientific American* refused to publish my response to this attack, but the response did appear in the March 1993 issue of *Perspectives on Science and Christian Faith*, the journal of the American Scientific Affiliation.

[7] Kuhn, Thomas S. *The Structure of Scientific Revolutions* 2nd ed., (Chicago: University of Chicago Press, 1970): 79.

[8] Hawking, Stephen. A *Brief History of Time: The Updated and Expanded Tenth Anniversary Edition* (New York: Bantam Books, 1996).

Chapter Two

—⁓—

THE BIG BANG,
STEPHEN HAWKING, AND GOD[1]

Henry F. Schaefer III

Since 1987, Dr. Henry F. Schaefer has been Graham Perdue Professor of Chemistry and Director of the Center for Computational Quantum Chemistry at the University of Georgia. Dr. Schaefer received his B. S. degree in Chemical Physics from the Massachusetts Institute of Technology (1966) and Ph.D. degree in Chemical Physics from Stanford University (1969). For 18 years (1969-1987) he served as Professor of Chemistry at the University of California, Berkeley. He is the author of more than 900 scientific publications, the majority appearing in the Journal of Chemical Physics or the Journal of the American Chemical Society.

Abstract

Stephen Hawking is now perhaps the world's best-known scientist. The sale of more than twenty million copies of his book A Brief History of Time is essentially without precedent for a book about science. Hawking's book, and the subject of cosmology more generally, pose many questions about the interface between science and theism, and some of these questions will be explored in this essay.

COSMOLOGY IS THE STUDY OF THE UNIVERSE AS A whole—its structure, origin, and development. The subjects cosmology addresses are profound, both scientifically and theologically. Perhaps the best way to define cosmology is in terms of the questions that it asks. Hugh Ross does an excellent job of stating these questions in his important book, *The Fingerprint of God:*[2]

1) Is our universe finite or infinite in size and content?
2) Has this universe been here forever or did it have a beginning?
3) Was the universe created?
4) If the universe was not created, how did it get here?
5) If the universe was created, how was this creation accomplished, and what can we learn about the agent and events of creation?
6) Who or what governs the laws and constants of physics?
7) Are such laws the products of chance or have they been designed?
8) How do the laws and constants of physics relate to the support and development of life?
9) Is there any knowable existence beyond the apparently observed dimensions of the universe?
10) Do we expect the universe to expand forever, or is a period of contraction to be followed by a big crunch?

The Big Bang

Let me begin by noting the relationship between my own research as a quantum chemist and the field of cosmology. On November 5, 1973, my research group published its first paper on interstellar molecules, the molecules that exist in those relatively empty regions between the stars. Our paper appeared in the journal *Nature* and was titled, "Theoretical Support for the Assignment of X-ogen to the HCO+ Molecular Ion." The motivation for research on interstellar molecules has largely derived from the suggestion that these are the elementary materials from which life might have originated. My research group has continued its interest in interstellar molecules over the years, with many of our papers being published in the *Astrophysical Journal*, considered by some to be the premier journal in the field. Our most recent paper in the field, titled, "Ion-Molecule Reactions Producing HC_3NH+ in Interstellar Space: Forbiddenness of the Reaction between Cyclic C_3H_3+ and the N Atom," appeared in the November 10, 1999 issue of the *Astrophysical Journal*. Three more recent astrophysical papers involving my research group are in various stages leading to publication.

The idea that the universe had a specific time of origin has been philosophically resisted by some very distinguished scientists . . . . For example, Arthur Eddington (1882-1944), who confirmed Einstein's general theory of relativity in 1919, later stated, "Philosophically, the notion of a beginning to the present order is repugnant to me. I should like to find a genuine loophole."

The idea that the universe had a specific time of origin has been philosophically resisted by some very distinguished scientists. Hugh Ross has done an excellent job of summarizing this resistance.[3] Ross begins with Arthur Eddington (1882-1944), who experimentally confirmed Einstein's (1879-1955) general theory of relativity in 1919. Eddington stated a dozen years later: "Philosophically, the notion of a beginning to the present order is repugnant to me. I should like to find a genuine loophole." Eddington later said, "We must allow evolution an infinite amount of time to get started."

Albert Einstein's response to the consequences of his own general theory of relativity may be reasonably interpreted to reflect a possible concern about the peril of a confrontation with the Creator. Through the equations of general relativity, we can trace the origin of the universe backward in time to some sort of a beginning. However, to evade this seemingly inevitable cosmological conclusion, Einstein introduced a cosmological constant, a "fudge factor," to yield a static model for the universe. He longed for a universe that was infinitely old. In fairness, Einstein later considered this to be one of the few serious mistakes of his scientific career. However, even this concession must have been painful, as Einstein had a strong conviction that all physical phenomena ultimately should be accounted for in terms of continuous fields everywhere.[4]

Einstein ultimately gave at best reluctant assent to what he called, "the necessity for a beginning" and eventually to "the presence of a superior reasoning power." But he never did embrace the concept of a personal Creator, a compassionate God who cares for men and women and children.

To understand the intensity of the objections to the idea that the universe had a beginning, an excursus may be helpful. Again following Hugh Ross[5], let us note the five traditional arguments for the existence of God. These arguments may be found in Augustine, and they were further elaborated by Thomas Aquinas. This may seem an unlikely starting point for our topic, but I think you will see as we proceed that these arguments keep coming up. I am not going to take a position on whether these arguments are valid, but I will state them, because throughout current discussions of cosmology these arguments are often cited:

1) The cosmological argument: the effect of the universe's existence must have a suitable cause.
2) The teleological argument: the design of the universe implies a purpose or direction behind it.
3) The rational argument: the operation of the universe according to order and natural law implies a mind behind it.
4) The ontological argument: man's ideas of God (his God-consciousness, if you like) implies a God who imprinted such a consciousness.
5) The moral argument: man's built-in sense of right and wrong can be accounted for only by an innate awareness of a code of law – an awareness implanted by a higher being.

So then, why has there been such resistance to the idea of a definite beginning of the universe? Much of it goes right back to that first argument, the cosmological argument. It may be useful to break down the cosmological argument into three parts:

(a) Everything that begins to exist must have a cause;
(b) If the universe began to exist, then
(c) The universe must have a cause.

You can see the direction this argument is flowing - a direction of discomfort to some physicists and others knowledgeable about these matters. Such a person was the Princeton physicist Robert Dicke, advocate of the infinitely oscillating theory of the universe, of which we will say more later. Dicke stated in 1965 that an infinitely old universe, "would relieve us of the necessity of understanding the origin of matter at any finite time in the past."[6]

In 1946 George Gamow (1904-1968), a Russian-born American physicist, proposed that the primeval fireball, the "Big Bang," was an intense concentration of pure energy. It was the source of all the matter that now exists in the universe. The Big Bang Theory predicts that all the galaxies in the universe should be rushing away from each other at high speeds as a result of that initial event, which some have described as a singular explosion. A possible future dictionary definition of the hot big bang theory encompasses the idea that the entire physical universe, all the matter and energy and even the four dimensions of time and space, burst forth from a state of infinite or near infinite density, temperature, and pressure.

The 1965 observation of the microwave background radiation by Arno Penzias (1933-) and Robert Wilson (1936-) of the Bell Telephone Laboratories (regrettably partially dismantled following the breakup of AT&T) convinced most scientists of the validity of the Big Bang Theory. Further observations reported in 1992 have moved the Big Bang Theory from a consensus view to the nearly unanimous view among cosmologists: there was an origin to the universe, perhaps 13-15 billion years ago. My former Berkeley colleague Joseph Silk and his coworkers gave a brief summary of the evidence for the Big Bang Theory in *Science* magazine:

> The hot big bang model is enormously successful. It
> provides the framework for understanding the expansion
> of the universe, the cosmic background radiation, and
> the primeval abundance of light elements, as well as a

general picture of how the structure seen in the universe today was formed.[7]

Many scientists have been willing to comment on the philosophical consequences of the Big Bang Theory. For example, Arno Penzias, co-discoverer of the microwave background radiation and 1978 Nobel Prize recipient in physics, stated to the *New York Times*:

> The best data we have (concerning the Big Bang) are exactly what I would have predicted, had I nothing to go on but the five books of Moses, the Psalms, the Bible as a whole.[8]

When asked more recently why some cosmologists were so affectionate in their embrace of the steady state theory (the idea that the universe is infinitely old) of the origin of the universe, Penzias responded: "Well, some people are uncomfortable with the purposefully created world. To come up with things that contradict purpose, they tend to speculate about things they haven't seen."[9]

"Well, some people are uncomfortable with the purposefully created world. To come up with things that contradict purpose, they tend to speculate about things they haven't seen."

Arno Penzias, *1978 Nobel Prize recipient in physics*

Perhaps the most amusing statement in this regard came from Cambridge University physicist Dennis Sciama, one of the most distinguished advocates of the steady state theory of the universe. Shortly after he gave up on the steady state hypothesis, Sciama stated: "The steady state theory has a sweep and beauty that for some unaccountable reason the architect of the universe appears to have overlooked."[10] Of course, we theoretical scientists have an abundance of excuses why our cherished theories sometimes fail. But the notion of blaming our failures on the "architect of the universe" is very creative.

It is an unusual day when newspapers all over the world devote their front page headlines to a story about science. But that is exactly what happened on April 24, 1992. Announced on that date were the results of the so-called "big bang ripples" observations made by the cosmic background explorer (COBE) satellite of NASA. These ripples are the small variations in the temperature of the universe (about 2.7 degrees Celsius above absolute zero) far from heavenly bodies.

These observations were remarkably consistent with the predictions of the Big Bang Theory. The particular item that the *London Times, New York Times*, etc. seemed to pick up on was a statement by George Smoot, the team leader from the Lawrence Berkeley Laboratory. Smoot said, "It's like looking at God."[11] For obvious reasons, this headline captured the attention of thinking people throughout the world. In the euphoria that followed, Stephen Hawking described the big bang ripples observations as "the scientific discovery of the century, if not all time."[12]

"These findings make the idea that God created the universe a more respectable hypothesis today than at any time in the last 100 years."

Frederick Burnham, *a science-historian*
quoted in the Los Angeles Times

A more sober assessment of the big bang ripples observations was given one week later in the *Los Angeles Times*. Frederick Burnham, a science-historian, said, "These findings, now available, make the idea that God created the universe a more respectable hypothesis today than at any time in the last 100 years."[13]

George Smoot, leader of the COBE team of scientists, and I were undergraduate classmates at M.I.T. We both arrived in September of 1962 and graduated in June of 1966. I do not remember meeting George Smoot, but his last name was famous within the M.I.T. community from the first day of our freshman year. However, the fame of the name Smoot would not suggest that George would become one of the world's most famous scientists 26 years following his graduation from M.I.T. In fact, about one-third of the undergraduate student body lived in social fraternities, which were located across the Charles River from M.I.T. I chose Sigma Alpha Epsilon and for you who believe American social fraternities excel primarily in drunkenness and debauchery, let it be notice that it took a full six years after graduation for me to become a Christian.

In 1958, Oliver R. Smoot, Jr., a new member of Lambda Chi Alpha, is said to have consumed an excessive amount of a common chemical reagent, namely ethyl alcohol. As the story goes, Smoot, at 5' 7" tall, and in a semi-conscious state was rolled across the Harvard Bridge by his fraternity mates numerous times. On the next day, the Harvard Bridge was smartly adorned with Smoot markers. At every ten Smoots (an interval of about 56 feet) brightly painted markers noted the achievement. The total length of the Harvard Bridge was boldly proclaimed at both ends to be 364.4 Smoots plus one ear.

During the 1963-1964 academic year, my fraternity decided that Smoot was getting far more credit than he deserved. One of our members, Fred Souk, declared that he was better than Smoot in every respect. So, we went out in the dark of night, painted out the Smoot marks, and replaced them with Souk marks. Fred was a bit taller than Smoot, so the total number of Souks did not quite match the old Smoots. As it turned out, this action enraged the members of the Lambda Chi Alpha fraternity. The Souk marks were obliterated the very next night, and replaced with the venerable Smoots, which continue to this date to be repainted regularly on the Harvard Bridge. I was surprised when I read George Smoot's semi-autobiographical popular book, *Wrinkles in Time*, about the big bang ripples, I found no mention of the celebrated achievement associated with his name, the immortal Smoot marks; however, on his web site George Smoot acknowledges that Oliver R. Smoot, Jr. is a "distant relative." Apparently, the only Smoots ever to attend M.I.T. were Oliver R. Smoot, Jr., George Smoot, and Oliver's son Stephen Smoot.

Not everyone was ecstatic about the Smoot observations that revealed the so-called "big bang ripples." Certainly, those who had argued so strongly and passionately for a steady state model of the universe did not appreciate the interpretation of these results. The latter group included most prominently two senior scientists, Sir Fred Hoyle (1915-2001), the British astronomer, and Geoffrey Burbidge (1925-), a distinguished astrophysicist at the University of California at San Diego.

We may continue to probe the philosophical implications of these big bang ripples observations by assessing a statement of Geoffrey Burbidge (made during a radio discussion with Hugh Ross) concerning these matters. Burbidge discounts the most obvious interpretation of the new experiments. He remains a strong advocate, in the face of seemingly overwhelming evidence, of the steady state theory. Remarkably, Burbidge stated that the COBE satellite experiments come from "the First Church of Christ of the Big Bang."[14]

Of course George Smoot took strong exception to this statement. In *Wrinkles in Time*, Smoot does write cautiously "There is no doubt that a parallel exists between the big bang as an event and the Christian notion of creation from nothing."[15] Burbidge did say something in the same interview that is indisputable, however. He predictably favored the steady state hypothesis and claimed that his view supports Hinduism and not Christianity. That is correct, because the steady state theory of the universe, were it to be true, would provide some support for the never ending cycles of existence taught by orthodox Hinduism.

Hugh Ross, an astrophysicist turned generalist, has written very persuasively on this topic. He again brings us to the philosophical implications. Ross states:

> By definition, time is that dimension in which cause and effect phenomena take place. If time's beginning is concurrent with the beginning of the universe, as the space-time theorem says, then the cause of the universe must be some entity operating in a time dimension completely independent of and pre-existent to the time dimension of the cosmos. This conclusion is powerfully important to our understanding of who God is and who or what God is not. It tells us that the creator is transcendent, operating beyond the dimensional limits of the universe. It tells us that God is not the universe itself, nor is God contained within the universe.[16]

Perhaps some readers are inclined to say "So what?" If you fall into that category, may I remind you that well more than one billion people on this planet believe either that God is the universe itself or that God is contained within the universe. If the Big Bang Theory is true, it creates serious philosophical problems for these worldviews. Some scientific discoveries do have profound metaphysical implications. An entire book on this subject, titled, *The Dancing Universe*, has been written by Dartmouth College physics professor Marcello Gleiser. Without displaying any theistic sympathies, Gleiser confirms much of what Ross states above. His flow chart labeled "A Classification of Cosmogonical Models" is of special interest. [17]

Gleiser asks the question, "Is there a beginning?" to provide a primary sorting of worldviews. On the left side of Gleiser's diagram a positive answer to the above question leads via a particular path to creation by the sovereign God of the universe, as described in Genesis. On the right hand side, a "no" answer in regard to a beginning leads by another path to a rhythmic universe, as perhaps exemplified by the dance of Shiva in Hinduism. The resistance of several streams of Hinduism to the Big Bang Theory was recently highlighted at a symposium sponsored by the American Association for the Advancement of Science (AAAS) in Washington, D.C. (April 1999). In prepared remarks Hindu philosopher Anindita Baslev of Aarhus University in Denmark quoted from the ancient texts of her religion and summarily dismissed the discussions of big bang mechanics as "cosmological speculations."

Following the remarkable financial success of Stephen Hawking's 1988 book, *A Brief History of Time*, a number of distinguished physicists tried their hand at the same literary genre. One such book is that by the brilliant physicist, Leon Lederman, a Nobel Prize winner and a gifted and dedicated educator. He wrote a book called *The God Particle* and, although the title sounds appealing, the best material is limited to the first few pages. The remainder of the book is largely a case for the building of the SSC, the Super Conducting Super Collider, a proposed massive particle accelerator near Waco, Texas, a project that died from lack of funding by the U.S. Congress in 1993. The first section is a good summary of what I have attempted to say in this lecture thus far. Leon Lederman states:

> "In the very beginning, there was a void—a curious
> form of vacuum—a nothingness containing no space,
> no time, no matter, no light, no sound. Yet the laws of

nature were in place and this curious vacuum held potential. A story logically begins at the beginning. But this story is about the universe and unfortunately there are no data for the very beginning. None, zero! We don't know anything about the universe until it reaches the mature age of a billionth of a trillionth of a second - that is, some very short time after the creation in the Big Bang. When you read or hear anything about the birth of the universe, someone is making it up. We are in the realm of philosophy. Only God knows what happened at the very beginning."[18]

"Only God knows what happened at the very beginning."

Leon Lederman, *Nobel Prize winner*
Quoted from his book The God Particle

In candid moments, outstanding cosmologists make statements similar to that quoted above. For example, Stephen Hawking states that, "The actual point of creation lies outside the scope of the presently known laws of physics."[19] M.I.T. professor Alan Guth, critical contributor to the "inflationary" understanding of the Big Bang Theory, is often considered the American counterpart of Hawking and has said analogously, "The instant of creation remains unexplained."[20]

Stephen Hawking

Stephen Hawking is probably the most famous living scientist. The tenth anniversary edition of his book, *A Brief History of Time,*[21] is available in paperback and I strongly recommend it. The book has sold in excess of 20 million copies. For such a book to sell so many copies is essentially unheard of in the history of science writing. For the past five years I have used *A Brief History of Time* as the centerpiece of a course that I teach for a select group of 15 University of Georgia freshmen. For balance, the class also studies the novel, *That Hideous Strength,*[22] the third book in the C. S. Lewis space trilogy. My course falls in the "Get to know the professor" category that is becoming popular in large public universities to offset the sense of anonymity that many entering freshmen feel.

An excellent film, *A Brief History of Time*,[23] directed by Errol Morris, has been made about the book with the same title and we enjoy the film every year in my freshman seminar. Hawking's wonderful sense of humor is displayed in the foreword of *A Reader's Companion*, a book about the film, stating, "This is the book of the film of the book. I don't know if they are planning a film of the book of the film of the book."[24]

I want to begin our discussion of Stephen Hawking by saying something about his scientific research, without getting bogged down in details. Hawking has made his well-deserved scientific reputation by investigating in great detail one particular set of problems: the singularity and horizons around black holes and at the beginning of time. Now, every writer in this general area is convinced that if you encountered a black hole, it would be the last thing you ever encountered. A black hole is a massive system so centrally condensed that the force of gravity prevents everything within it, including light, from escaping. The reassuring thing is that, despite what our children see on the Saturday morning cartoons, no black hole appears to be in our neighborhood. That is, the closest black hole to planet earth is more distant than could be traveled in the lifetime of a human being using conventional rockets.

Stephen Hawking's first major scientific work was published with Roger Penrose (a physicist very famous in his own right) and George Ellis (not as famous as Penrose and Hawking, but still very well known), during the period 1968-1970. They demonstrated that every solution to the equations of general relativity guarantees the existence of a singular boundary for space and time in the past. This landmark is now known as the "singularity theorem," and is a tremendously important finding, being about as close as we can get to a mathematical rationalization for the Big Bang Theory. Later, of course, Hawking began to carry out independent research, both by himself and with his own doctoral students and postdoctoral fellows. As early as 1973, he began to formulate ideas about the quantum evaporation of black holes, exploding black holes, "Hawking radiation," and so on. Some of Hawking's work is radical, exploratory, and even speculative in nature. However, by any reasonable standard Stephen Hawking is a great scientist. Even if time shows some of his more radical proposals to be incorrect, Hawking will have had a profound impact on the history of science.

The scientific centerpiece of *A Brief History of Time* would appear to fall in the speculative category of his research. In fact, I think it is fair to say that the scientific centerpiece of *A Brief History of Time* was not considered one of Hawking's most important papers prior to the publication of the book in 1987. I am referring to the "no boundary proposal" that Hawking published in 1984 in work with James Hartle, a physics professor at the University of California at Santa Barbara.[25] Using a grossly simplified picture of the universe in conjunction with an elegant vacuum fluctuation model, Hartle and Hawking were able to provide a mathematical rationalization for the entire universe popping into existence at the beginning of time. This model has also been called the "universe as a wave function" and the "no beginning point." While such mathematical exercises are highly speculative, they may eventually lead us to a deeper understanding of the creation event. I postpone my analysis of the no boundary proposal for a few pages.

Hawking is certainly the most famous physicist in history who has not won the Nobel Prize. This has puzzled some people. Many people automatically assume that Professor Hawking has already won the Nobel Prize. Yet, as of this writing (late 2002), he has not. This is probably because the Swedish Royal Academy demands that an award-winning discovery must be supported by verifiable experimental or observational evidence. Hawking's work to date remains largely unconfirmed. Although the mathematics and concepts of his theories are certainly beautiful and elegant, science waited until 1994 for rock solid evidence for even the existence of black holes. The verification of Hawking radiation or any of his more radical theoretical proposals still seems far off. In this context, we must recall that Albert Einstein was wrong about a number of important things scientific, especially quantum mechanics; yet we recognize him as one of the three great physicists of all time, along with Isaac Newton and James Clerk Maxwell. I also want to mention that a number of Nobel Prize Committees have shown themselves to be composed of rather savvy people, capable of compromise. So I would not be surprised to see the old gentlemen in Stockholm find a way to award the Nobel Prize in Physics to Stephen Hawking. Perhaps

Hawking could share the prize with those responsible for the first observations of black holes.

Those who have not read A Brief History of Time may be surprised to find that the book has a main character and that main character is God.... To put Stephen Hawking's opinions about God in some sort of a context, he seems to have made up his mind about God long before he became a cosmologist.

God

Those who have not read *A Brief History of Time* may be surprised to find that the book has a main character. That main character is God. This was the feature of the book that the well-known atheist Carl Sagan found distressing. Sagan wrote the preface to the first edition of the book, but was less famous than Hawking by the time of arrival of the tenth anniversary edition, in which Sagan's preface does not appear. God is discussed in *A Brief History of Time* from near the beginning all the way to the crescendo of the final sentence. So let us try to put Hawking's opinions about God in some sort of a context. The context is that Stephen Hawking seems to have made up his mind about God long before he became a cosmologist.

Not surprisingly, the principal influence in Stephen's early life was his mother, Isobel. Isobel Hawking was a member of the Communist Party in England in the 1930's, and her son has carried some of that intellectual tradition right through his life. Incidentally, Hawking's fame is now such that he felt obligated to endorse one of the candidates in the 2000 United States presidential election. By the time he was 13, Hawking's hero was the brilliant agnostic philosopher and mathematician, Bertrand Russell. At the same age, two of Hawking's friends became Christians as a result of the 1955 Billy Graham London campaign. According to his biographers,[26] Hawking stood apart from these encounters with "a certain amused detachment." There is little in *A Brief History of Time* that deviates in a significant way from what we know of the religious views of the 13-year-old Stephen Hawking.

However, we must note that in public questioning Hawking insists that he is not an atheist. And eyewitness observers tell me that in recent years Stephen Hawking has appeared "once or twice a month" in an Anglican church with his second wife.

Perhaps the most important event of Stephen Hawking's life occurred on December 31, 1962. He met his future wife of 25 years, Jane Wilde, at a New Year's Eve party. One month later, Hawking was diagnosed with a debilitating disease, ALS or amyotrophic lateral sclerosis, known in North America as Lou Gehrig's disease. He was given two years to live at the time. That was nearly 40 years ago. I have seen three chemistry professor friends die of this terrible disease. My three friends lasted two, three, and five years, respectively, the last surviving on an iron lung for his last tortuous year. By anyone's estimation, the preservation of Stephen Hawking's life is a medical miracle. And he is a man of great personal courage.

At this point in his life (1962), Stephen was by all accounts an average-performing graduate student at Cambridge University, but even average doctoral students at Cambridge, still one of the five great universities in the world, are very good. Let me quote from his biographers, White and Gribbon, on this point:

> However, there is little doubt that Jane Wilde's appearance on the scene was a major turning point in Stephen Hawking's life. The two of them began to see a lot more of one another and a strong relationship developed. It was finding Jane Wilde that enabled him to break out of his depression and regenerate some belief in his life and work. For Hawking, his engagement to Jane was probably the most important thing that ever happened to him. It changed his life, gave him something to live for and made him determined to live. Without the help that Jane gave him, he would almost certainly not have been able to carry on or had the will to do so.[27]

They married in July of 1965, somewhat past the expected date of Stephen Hawking's death. The fact that three children followed is indisputable evidence that Stephen was not dead at all. In an interview shortly following the publication of *A Brief History of Time*, Hawking himself said, "what really made a difference was that I got engaged to a woman named Jane Wilde. This gave me something to live for."[28] Jane Wilde is an interesting person in her own right. I think she decided early on to pursue an academic discipline as far as possible from her husband. She received a doctorate for her research on the medieval lyric poetry of the Iberian Peninsula.

Jane Hawking is a Christian. She made the following statement in 1989,

> Without my faith in God, I wouldn't have been able to live in this situation (namely, the deteriorating health of her husband, with no obvious income but that of a Cambridge don to live on). I would not have been able to marry Stephen in the first place because I wouldn't have had the optimism to carry me through, and I wouldn't have been able to carry on with it.[29]

The reason the book has sold more than 20 million copies, i.e., the reason for Hawking's success as a popularizer of science, is that he addresses the problems of meaning and purpose that concern all thinking people. The book overlaps with Christian belief and it does so deliberately, but graciously and without rancor. It is an important book that needs to be treated with respect and attention. There is no reason to agree with everything put forth in *A Brief History of Time* and you will see that I have a couple of areas of disagreement. It has been argued that this is the most widely unread book in the history of literature. I first began to prepare this material for a lecture in December 1992, because I was asked by a friend (John Mason) in Australia to come and speak on the subject. John wrote to me, "A great many people in Sydney have purchased this book. Some claim to have read it." So I encourage you to join the students in my University of Georgia class and become one of those who have actually read *A Brief History of Time*.

Stephen Hawking has made some eminently sensible statements on the relationship between science and Christianity. For example,

> It is difficult to discuss the beginning of the universe without mentioning the concept of God. My work on the origin of the universe is on the borderline between science and religion, but I try to stay on the scientific side of the border. It is quite possible that God acts in ways that cannot be described by scientific laws.[30]

When asked by a reporter whether he believed that science and Christianity were competing worldviews, Hawking replied cleverly, "Then Newton would not have discovered the law of gravity." Dr. Hawking is well aware that Newton had strong religious convictions.

A Brief History of Time makes wonderfully ambiguous statements such as,

> Even if there is only one possible unified theory (here he is alluding to the envisioned unification of our understandings of quantum mechanics and gravity), it is just a set of rules and equations. What is it that breathes fire into the equations and makes a universe for them to describe? [31]

In a similar vein Hawking asks, "Why does the universe go to the bother of existing?" Although Hawking does not attempt to answer these two critical questions, they make wonderful discussion topics for university students, and I have enjoyed using them for this purpose.

Hawking pokes fun at Albert Einstein for not believing in quantum mechanics. When asked why he didn't believe in quantum mechanics, Einstein would sometimes say things like "God doesn't play dice with the universe." On one such occasion, Niels Bohr is said to have responded, "Albert, stop telling God what He can do." Hawking's adroit response to Einstein is that "God not only plays dice. He sometimes throws them where they can't be seen." Of course, I like Hawking's response very much, having devoted my professional career to the study of molecular quantum mechanics.

For me (and for Hawking's now distinguished student Don Page, whom I will discuss more later) the most precious jewel in *A Brief*

History of Time reflects Hawking's interest in the writing's of Augustine of Hippo (354-430 A.D.). Hawking states,

> The idea that God might want to change His mind is an example of the fallacy, pointed out St. Augustine, of imagining God as a being existing in time. Time is a property only of the universe that God created. Presumably, God knew what He intended when He set it up.[32]

After reading 100 pages the first time through A Brief History of Time, I thought, "This is a great book; Hawking is building a splendid case for creation by an intelligent being." But, things then changed and I realized this magnificent cosmological epic was adulterated by poor philosophy and theology.

The first time I read *A Brief History of Time*, admittedly not critically, for the first 100 pages or so I thought, "This is a great book; Hawking is building a splendid case for creation by an intelligent being." But, things then changed and I realized this magnificent cosmological epic was adulterated by poor philosophy and theology. For example, Hawking writes in the first edition, "These laws (of physics) may have originally been decreed by God, but it appears that He has since left the universe to evolve according to them and does not now intervene in it."[33] The grounds on which Hawking claims "it appears" are unstated, and his conception of god is certainly not the God revealed in time and space and history. What follows is a curious mixture of deism and the ubiquitous "god of the gaps." Stephen Hawking thus appears uncertain (agnostic) of his belief in a god of his own creation.

Now, lest any reader be uncertain, let me emphasize that Hawking strenuously denies charges that he is an atheist. When he is accused of atheism, he is affronted and says that such assertions are not true. For example, Hawking has stated "I thought I had left the question of the existence of a Supreme Being completely open....It would be perfectly consistent with all we know to say that there was a Being who was responsible for all the laws of physics." [34] Stephen Hawking is probably an agnostic or a deist (a believer in an impersonal god) or something in between these two positions, his recent church attendance notwithstanding. He is certainly not an atheist and sometimes does not even appear very sympathetic to atheism.

One statement frequently quoted from *A Brief History of Time* is,

> So long as the universe had a beginning, we would suppose it had a creator (the cosmological argument). But if the universe is really completely self-contained, having no boundary or edge, it would have neither beginning nor end: it would simply be. What place, then, for a creator?[35]

Hawking's most famous statement is contained in the last paragraph of *A Brief History of Time*. Perhaps attempting to balance the quotation just cited, Hawking writes "However, if we do discover a complete theory . . . then we would know the mind of God." As a person who has dedicated his professional life to science, I am personally sympathetic to this statement. John Calvin correctly stated, "All truth is God's truth."[36] But, Professor Hawking is claiming too much. I would modify his statement to say that if we had a unified, complete theory of physics, we would know *much more* about the mind of God. To claim to know God comprehensively is beyond the capability of any human being.

The Anthropic Principle

I feel the necessity to say something here about the anthropic principle. One statement of the anthropic principle would be that there are a number of fundamental constants (for example, the mass of the electron) or derived scientific parameters (for example, the dipole moment of the water molecule), any one of which changed just a little bit, would make the earth uninhabitable by human beings. In this regard, a book I strongly recommend is *The Creator and the Cosmos*[37] by Hugh Ross. Ross has a substantial discussion of the anthropic principle and demonstrates why many physicists and astronomers have considered the possibility that the universe not only was divinely caused, but in fact divinely designed.

One such person is Amherst College astronomy professor George Greenstein (a pantheist or something similar), who makes this statement:

> As we survey all the evidence, the thought insistently arises that some supernatural agency, or rather Agency, must be involved. Is it possible that suddenly, without intending to, we have stumbled upon scientific proof of the existence of a Supreme Being? Was it God who stepped in and so providentially created the cosmos for our benefit? [38]

Personally, I fear that Greenstein has gone, relative to Hawking, too far in the other direction. We do not have indisputable scientific proof of the existence of God. But, I am convinced that we do have, in the big bang understanding, some very good evidence for the existence of the transcendent God of the universe.

Others have commented, sometimes inadvertently, on this evidence. A book I recommend is, *Dreams of a Final Theory* by Steven Weinberg (1933-), winner of the Nobel Prize in Physics in 1979 and considered by many to be the greatest physicist of the last half of the twentieth century). Although Steven Weinberg is a staunch atheist, Chapter XI of his book is titled "What About God?" Therein, Weinberg tells a story related by the Venerable Bede (672-735), English theologian and historian. In the story, a speech is made before King Edwin of Northumbria in favor of the adoption of Christianity. In this speech the term "banqueting hall" is used to describe the ordinary existence of human beings on planet earth. Weinberg's perceptive comment on the speech is, "It is an almost irresistible temptation to believe with Bede and Edwin that there must be something for us outside the banqueting hall."[39] There must be something beyond strict reductionism or materialism. This view is echoed in the New Testament. For example, St. Paul wrote, "Ever since the creation of the world, God's eternal power and divine nature, invisible though they are, have been understood and seen through the things He has made" (Letter to the Romans 1:20). This is essentially what Steven Weinberg is attempting to describe—that almost "irresistible temptation" to believe in God.

It is relatively unusual that a physical scientist is truly an atheist. Why is this true? Some point to the anthropic constraints, the remarkable fine tuning of the universe. For example, Freeman Dyson, a Princeton faculty member, has said, "Nature has been kinder to us that we had any right to expect." [40] Martin Rees, one of Hawking's colleagues at Cambridge, notes the same facts when he recently stated,

> The possibility of life as we know it depends on the values of a few basic, physical constants and is in some respects remarkably sensitive to their numerical values. Nature does exhibit remarkable coincidences. [41]

Science writer extraordinaire Paul Davies adds,

> There is for me powerful evidence that there is something going on behind it all.... It seems as though somebody has fine tuned nature's numbers to make the Universe.... The impression of design is overwhelming. [42]

Some scientists express surprise at what they view as "accidental occurrences." However, this astonishment quickly disappears when one sees purpose instead of arbitrary laws of nature.

Some scientists express surprise at what they view as so many "accidental occurrences." However, this astonishment quickly disappears when one sees purpose instead of arbitrary laws of nature.

Against powerful logic, some atheists continue to claim, irrespective of the anthropic constraints, that the universe and human life were created by chance. The main argument seems to be "Since we human beings are here, it must have happened in a purely reductionist manner." This argument strikes me like the apocryphal response of a person waking up in the morning to find an elephant in his or her bedroom and concluding that this is no surprise since the probability of the elephant being in the bedroom is a perfect 100%. Obviously this is a philosophical rather than scientific response to the situation.

A reply to this argument has been developed by the philosopher/historian William Lane Craig. The atheist's argument states that since we're here, we know every element of the creation must have happened by strictly material forces. Craig's philosophical counterargument goes like this: Suppose a dozen sharpshooters are sent to execute a prisoner by firing squad. They all shoot a number of rounds in just the right direction, but the prisoner escapes unharmed. The prisoner could conclude, since he is alive, that all the sharpshooters missed by some extremely unlikely chance. He may wish to attribute his survival to some remarkable piece of good luck. But he would be far more rational to conclude that the guns were loaded with blanks or that the sharpshooters had all deliberately missed. Not only is life itself overwhelmingly improbable, but its appearance almost immediately (in geological terms), perhaps within as short a period as 10 million years following the solidification and cooling of our once-molten planet, defies explanation by conventional physical and chemical laws.[43]

The No Boundary Proposal

Let us return to Hawking's no boundary proposal—the idea that the universe has neither beginning nor end. By treating the universe as a wave function, Hawking hopes to rationalize the universe's popping into existence 12-15 billion years ago. Critical to Hawking's research in this regard is the notion of imaginary time. The concept of imaginary time is a powerful mathematical device used on occasion by theoretical chemists and physicists. I remember clearly the day in the autumn of 1965, during my Complex Variables class as a senior at M.I.T., when I learned that the result of contour integration was two pi i times the sum of the residues.

For me, it was about as close to a revelation as I had received up to that time in my life. My closest colleague at Berkeley, Professor William H. Miller, in 1969 used imaginary time to understand the dynamics of chemical reactions, and it made him a household word in the world of science. The use of imaginary time is indeed a powerful tool.

Indulge me while I attempt to convey the essence of how imaginary time is exploited in theoretical physics and chemistry. One approaches a well-defined problem, with all variables necessarily being real. This means, for example, real positions for all particles, real velocities, and so on. Real problems begin with all quantities real. Then one undertakes a carefully chosen excursion into the complex plane, making one or more variables complex. Subsequently we do some really cool things mathematically. Finally, all the variables revert to real values, and we find that something important has been mathematically derived that would have otherwise been impossible to prove.

Hawking and Hartle's "no boundary" proposal begins by adopting a grossly oversimplified model of the universe. Then the authors make time imaginary, and prove in their terribly restricted model that the universe has neither beginning nor end. The flaw in the exercise is that the authors never go back to real time. Thus the notion that the universe has neither beginning nor end is something that exists in mathematical terms only. In real time, to which we as human beings are necessarily attached, rather than in Hawking's use of imaginary time, there will always be a singularity, that is, a beginning of time.

In an obviously contradictory statement in *A Brief History of Time*, Hawking actually concedes this point. What we are seeing in this situation is Hawking versus Hawking. I view the following statement as Hawking speaking in his right mind: "When one goes back to the real time in which we live, however, there will still appear to be singularities ...... In real time, the universe has a beginning and an end at singularities that form a boundary to space-time and at which the laws of science break down."[44] Only if we lived in imaginary time (not coming soon to a neighborhood near you!) would we encounter no singularities. In real time the universe was created ex nihilo 13-15 billion years ago.

With some trepidation, I will venture further. A case can be made that the Hartle-Hawking "no boundary proposal" is only of marginal scientific interest. The reasons for this conclusion might include: (a) the theory is a mathematical construct that has no unique empirical support; (b) the theory makes no verifiable scientific predictions that were not achieved earlier with simpler models; (c) the theory generates no significant research agenda. The primary purpose of the theory seems to be an attempt to evade the cosmological argument for the existence of God, via the claim that nature is self-contained and effectively eternal.

Science is primarily concerned with facts, not motive. Thus a complete scientific description of the creation does not necessarily rule out a providential account at the same time.

Science is primarily concerned with facts, not motive, and thus a complete scientific description of the creation does not necessarily rule out a providential account at the same time. William Paley's famous design argument suggests that if you are taking a walk in the woods and find a watch on the path, you should not conclude that the watch just assembled itself – despite the fact that we can take the watch apart, look at every single part and completely understand how it works. We look at the watch on the path and prudently conclude that it was designed by some higher intelligence.

In *A Brief History of Time*, Hawking states, "If the no boundary proposal is correct, He [God] had no freedom at all to choose initial conditions."[45] This statement strikes me as a leap into irrationality. Why does Hawking find, within the functioning of the universe, aspects that appear to him to be limitations of God's power? This stems not from any attitude of an infinite God, but rather from the attributes of finite man. Namely, we as human beings are able to scientifically discern characteristics of the Creator only as they are related to that which is created, that which we can observe. This limitation of ours immediately reduces what might be infinite to the finiteness of our existence. Of course, Biblically, there is no problem in accepting divine constraints to divine options, if the Creator chooses to run the universe according to His stated and established laws. Divine tenacity to His own laws is, of course, the very essence of the biblical God.

Another of Hawking's controversial statements needs to be addressed. Although it is not original with him, Hawking states: "We are such insignificant creatures on a minor planet of a very average star in the outer suburbs of one of a hundred billion galaxies. So it is difficult to believe in a God that would care about us or even notice our existence."[46] I take a different position. In their recent writings, Hugh Ross and Guillermo Gonzalez (a professor of astronomy at Iowa State University) have demonstrated that our solar system, and in particular the sun and planet earth, are in fact quite extraordinary in many respects. Further, there is no compelling evidence to date that life exists elsewhere in the universe. Human beings, thus far, appear to be the most advanced species in the universe. Maybe God does care about us! Stephen Hawking surveys the cosmos and concludes that the principal characteristic of humankind is obscurity. I consider the same evidence and conclude that human beings are special. I must be quick to add that a Christian worldview does not exclude the possibility of life, even sentient life, elsewhere in the universe. C.S. Lewis precisely addressed this possibility in his two science fiction novels, *Out of the Silent Planet* and *Perelandra*.

Stephen Hawking surveys the cosmos and concludes that the principal characteristic of humankind is obscurity. I consider the same evidence and conclude that human beings are special.

Before moving on, two related issues need to be addressed. *The first* concerns the infinitely oscillating model of the universe, which posits a ceaseless sequence of big bang/big crunch pairs. This model, popularized by Robert Dicke, makes the universe effectively eternal. The infinitely oscillating universe model, as noted above, comports nicely with Hinduism's dance of Shiva. Since the hypothesized period between the present big bang and its imagined big crunch would be just one of an infinite number of such periods, any problems relating to the time scale that might be needed for evolution are resolved by the conclusion that our interval must be "just right." On many occasions when I have presented this lecture, the Q&A time includes a question concerning this cosmological model. Actually, this issue was resolved for most cosmologists in 1983 in a critical paper by Alan Guth (best known for his pioneering work on the inflationary features of the Big Bang Theory). The title of Guth's paper tells the story: "The Impossibility of a Bouncing Universe."[47] Guth showed that even if the universe contained sufficient mass to halt the current expansion, any collapse would end in a thud, not a bounce. Incidentally, the weight of opinion among cosmologists has shifted over the past five years to the position that, short of direct intervention by God, the universe will continue to expand forever.

The second, and perhaps most recent, attempt to evade the (theistic) logical consequences of the fine-tuning of the universe (anthropic constraints) is the proposal that there are an infinite number of universes. This proposal has been given wide attention through the popular book *Just Six Numbers* by Martin Rees.[48] Rees's logic flows something like this:

a) he concedes that a universe like ours is overwhelmingly improbable; but
b) we know that God doesn't exist, or if He does He had nothing to do with the design of the universe;
c) thus there must be a near infinite number of universes;
d) ours happens to be the universe that is just right for human life.

Since no evidence for other universes is provided, Rees's argument is less than convincing, particularly for those who are prepared to consider the possibility of the existence of a personal God. The Rees proposal might be broadened a bit by adding that other universes might have their own forms of intelligent conscious life, very different from what is observed on planet earth. One could go further and state that there is no need for life in the proposed other universes to be based on carbon. John Polkinghorne responded to these ideas as follows:

> Those who make such a claim are drawing a very large intellectual blank check on a totally unknown bank account. Consciousness seems to demand very great physical complexity to sustain it (the human brain is the most complicated physical system we have encountered). It is far from persuasive that there are many alternative routes to the generation of such complexity.[49]

Rodney Holder critiques the postulation of the existence of many universes as an alternative to design in his paper published in *Science & Christian Belief*.[50] Holder states some of the problems associated with the postulate of an infinite number of universes:

a) the existence of infinitely many universes depends critically on parameter choices;
b) the probability that any universe in an ensemble is fine-tuned for life is zero;
c) the physical realization of any ensemble will exclude an infinity of possibilities;
e) the hypothesis is untestable and unscientific;
f) The hypothesis is not consistent with the amount of order found in our universe, nor with the persistence of order.

In summarizing this section, I suggest that a Christian worldview does not exclude the possibility of other universes. One of the great hymns of the Christian faith begins with the words, "O Lord my God, when I in awesome wonder, consider all the worlds Thy hands have made."[51] However a plausible scientific case for an infinite or near infinite number of universes has yet to be made.

A Broader View

Does everyone agree with Stephen Hawking concerning the metaphysical consequences of recent cosmological discoveries? Certainly not. Alan Lightman, an MIT professor with no obvious theistic inclinations, states in his book, "Contrary to popular myths, scientists appear to have the same range of attitudes about religious matters as does the general public."[52] This fact can be established either from anecdotes or from statistical data. Sigma Xi, the scientific honorary society, conducted a systematic poll a few years ago that showed that, on any given Sunday, around 41 percent of all Ph.D. scientists are in church; for the general population the figure is perhaps 42 percent. So, whatever influences people in their beliefs about God, it does not appear to have much to do with having a Ph.D. in science.

"Contrary to popular myths, scientists appear to have the same range of attitudes about religious matters as does the general public."

Alan Lightman, *MIT professor with no obvious theistic inclinations*

It is true in science, as well as in essentially all other professions, that after income levels reach perhaps $50,000 per year (in North America), further increases in salary may be correlated with higher percentages of agnosticism. In his paper in *Nature*, Edward Larson showed that for incomes above $150,000 per year, belief in God falls off significantly.[53] The same trend holds, for example, for lawyers at these income levels. This finding, of course, is consistent with the words of Jesus on the difficulty of a rich person entering the kingdom of heaven.

There are many prominent scientific counterexamples to Stephen Hawking. One is my former colleague at Berkeley for 18 years, Charles Townes. Townes won the Nobel Prize in Physics in 1964 for discovering the maser, which led quickly to the laser, surely one of the most important scientific advances of the twentieth century. In a statement from his recent book *Making Waves*, Professor Townes appears to take dead aim on Hawking by stating, "In my view, the question of origin seems to be left unanswered if we explore from a scientific view alone. Thus, I believe there is a need for some religious or metaphysical explanation. I believe in the concept of God and in His existence."[54]

Arthur Schawlow (1921-1999) was another Physics Nobel Prize winner (1981), honored for his work in laser spectroscopy. Schawlow was a professor at Stanford until his recent death and did not hesitate to identify himself as a Protestant Christian. He stated, "We are fortunate to have the Bible and especially the New Testament, which tells us so much about God in widely accessible human terms."[55]

I view this statement as uniquely scientific, knowing that Professor Schawlow was convinced that his discoveries in laser spectroscopy were telling him something about God's handiwork. However, unlike the New Testament, Schawlow's research was difficult to express in "widely accessible human terms."

For much of Hawking's career, the other chaired Professor of Theoretical Physics at Cambridge was John Polkinghorne, a nuclear physicist. He left the chair of mathematical physics at Cambridge in 1979 in order to train for the ordained ministry of the Church of England. Upon ordination, Polkinghorne became a parish priest for five years. He returned to Cambridge in 1986 as Dean of Trinity Hall and subsequently President of Queens' College. I am very familiar with the grounds of Queens' College, as it is immediately adjacent to St. Catherine's College, where I stay in Cambridge courtesy of my longtime collaborator, Professor Nicholas Handy. John Polkinghorne's statement of belief is straightforward: "I am a Christian believer and believe that God exists and has made Himself known in human terms in Jesus Christ."[56]

Probably the world's greatest living observational cosmologist is Allan Sandage. Sandage works in Pasadena, California at the Carnegie Observatories. In 1991 he received the Craford Prize, given by the Royal Swedish Academy every six years for cosmology and worth the same amount of money as the Nobel Prize (there is no Nobel Prize given for cosmology). Sandage has been called "the grand old man of cosmology" by the *New York Times*[57] and is viewed as the successor to his mentor, Edwin Hubble (1889-1953), who is considered the father of modern cosmology.

At about the age of 50, Sandage became a Christian. Sandage has stated "The nature of God is not to be found within any part of the findings of science. For that, one must turn to the Scriptures."[58] When asked the famous question regarding whether it is possible to be a scientist and a Christian, Sandage replied, "Yes. The world is too complicated in all its parts and interconnections to be due to chance alone. I am convinced that the existence of life with all its order in each of its organisms is simply too well put together."[59]

Of Hawking's two earliest collaborators (1970, the singularity theorem), Roger Penrose seems to be some sort of an unconventional theist, while George Ellis is a Christian. Ellis is Professor of Applied Mathematics at the University of Cape Town, South Africa. In the book, *Quantum Cosmology and the Laws of Nature*,[60] Ellis states his position with respect to ultimate questions:

1) God is the creator and sustainer of the universe and of humankind, transcending the universe but immanent in it;

2) God's nature embodies justice and holiness, but is also a personal and loving God who cares for each creature (so the name "father" is indeed appropriate);

3) God's nature is revealed most perfectly in the life and teachings of Jesus of Nazareth, as recorded in the New Testament of the Bible, who was sent by God to reveal the divine nature, summarized in "God is Love;"

4) God has an active presence in the world that still touches the lives of the faithful today.

One of the scientists closest to Stephen Hawking and prominent in the movie about *A Brief History of Time* is Donald Page. Page is Professor of Physics at the University of Alberta, where he hosted my lecture on this topic in July 1997. Our discussions following my lecture lasted for four hours spread over three days.

Don Page has had an excellent physics career in quantum cosmology in his own right, but he began to achieve fame as a postdoctoral fellow with Stephen Hawking. The Hawkings were not financially well off in the years prior to publication of his best selling book and needed some help to keep going. Don Page went to live with the Hawkings for the period 1976-1979.

Page is quoted concerning these years in the book (the book about the film about the book!):

> I would usually get up around 7:15 or 7:30 AM, take a shower, read in my Bible and pray. Then I would go down at 8:15 and get Stephen up. At breakfast, I would often tell him what I'd been reading in the Bible, hoping that maybe this would eventually have some influence. I remember telling Stephen one story about how Jesus had seen the deranged man, and how this man had these demons, and the demons asked that they be sent into a herd of swine. The swine then plunged over the edge of the cliff and into the sea. Stephen piped up and said, 'Well, the Society for the

Prevention of Cruelty to Animals would not like that story, would they!'[61]

Page has also stated:

> I am a conservative Christian in the sense of pretty much taking the Bible seriously for what it says. Of course, I know that certain parts are not intended to be read literally, so I am not precisely a literalist. But, I try to believe in the meaning I think it is intended to have.[62]

Expressing the universal yearning of theoretical physicists for simplicity in their methods, Page makes an interesting connection to the spiritual world:

> If the universe basically is very simple, the theological implications of this would need to be worked out. Perhaps the mathematical simplicity of the universe is a reflection of the personal simplicity of the Gospel message, that God sent His Son Jesus Christ to bridge the gap between Himself and each of us, who have rejected God or rejected what He wants for us by rebelling against His will and disobeying Him. This is a message simple enough even to be understood by children.[63]

My final example is Chris Isham, Professor of Theoretical Physics at Imperial College of Science and Technology, University of London. The superb popular writer and former research physicist Paul Davies has described Isham as "Britain's greatest quantum gravity expert." This is high praise indeed when one considers that Stephen Hawking's research area is quantum gravity. I had the pleasure of chatting with Professor Isham for a while after I gave this lecture at Imperial College in May, 2000.

Alluding to the philosopher Paul Tillich, Chris Isham states, "The God of Christianity is not only 'the ground of being.' He is also

Incarnate." Essential therein "is the vision of the Resurrection (of Jesus Christ) as 'the new creation out of the old order' and . . . the profound notion of the 'redemption of time' through the life and death of Jesus Christ. I think it will be rather a long time before theoretical physics has anything useful to add to that." [64]

Chris Isham is not belittling the importance of theoretical physics at all. He has committed his entire professional life to the pursuit of theoretical physics and he is passionate about it. But, he is saying that what he found in Jesus Christ surpasses anything that physics could hope to provide in terms of ultimate meaning.

Chris Isham is not belittling the importance of theoretical physics at all. He has committed his entire professional life to the pursuit of theoretical physics and he is passionate about it. But, he is *saying* that what he found in Jesus Christ surpasses anything that physics could hope to provide in terms of ultimate meaning.

The Limits of Science

A statement I think gives some balance to this discussion was made by one of my scientific heroes, Erwin Schrödinger, after whom the most important equation in science is named: the Schrödinger Equation. I have spent a good bit of my professional life trying to solve this equation for atoms and molecules. Toward the end of Schrödinger's career he began to write more expansively. His book *What is Life?* [65] is thought to have inspired an entire generation of molecular biologists. I would like to quote from Schrödinger's book, *Nature and the Greeks*. In it he takes a dim view of what we might call scientific imperialism. The Schrödinger statement in question is:

> I am very astonished that the scientific picture of the
> real world around me is very deficient. It gives us a lot
> of factual information, puts all of our experience in a
> magnificently consistent order, but it is ghastly silent

about all and sundry that is really near to our heart that really matters to us. It cannot tell us a word about red and blue, bitter and sweet, physical pain and physical delight; it knows nothing of beautiful and ugly, good or bad, God and eternity. Science sometimes pretends to answer questions in these domains but the answers are very often so silly that we are not inclined to take them seriously.[66]

Although science is an inspiring pursuit in its proper domain, it is not the whole story. Jane Hawking commented on this aspect of her husband's work following the publication of *A Brief History of Time*. She said:

Stephen has the feelings that because everything is reduced to a rational, mathematical formula, that must be the truth. He is delving into realms that really do matter to thinking people and, in a way that can have a very disturbing effect on people—and he's not competent.[67]

In a similar vein, my longtime friend and Berkeley faculty colleague, Phillip Johnson writes:

The irony of the situation is that Hawking's professional life currently is devoted to telling a story about the cosmos in which the elements that make his life interesting— love, faith, courage, and even creative imagination— disappear from view. Aspiring to know the mind of God, he can imagine nothing more interesting than a set of equations governing the movement of particles. A unified field theory would be a major scientific accomplishment, of course. But to Hawking it is just a step toward a distant but attainable goal of what he calls 'a complete understanding of the events around us, and of our own existence.' The way to this goal does not seem to require reading the Bible or Shakespeare, living in a variety of cultures, experiencing art, climbing mountains, or falling in love and having children. All it involves is 'the intellectually challenging task of developing better approximation methods.'[68]

Although Phil does not seem to appreciate the great affection with which persons such as Hawking and I hold equations, there is much that is worthy of consideration in Professor Johnson's analysis.

Richard Feynman states in his book *The Character of Physical Law*, that,

> Everything in physical science is a lot of protons, neutrons and electrons (parenthetical remark by HFS—and don't we love them, especially electrons!), while in daily life, we talk about men and history, or beauty and hope. Which is nearer to God—beauty and hope or the fundamental laws? To stand at either end, and to walk off that end of the pier only, hoping that out in that direction is a complete understanding, is a mistake.[69]

I would have to say that, at least in the final sentence of *A Brief History of Time*, Stephen Hawking has walked off one end of Feynman's pier.

Where Do We Go from Here?

In his book, *The Fingerprint of God*,[70] Hugh Ross seeks to construct a bridge between cosmology and matters of ultimate importance. With minor modifications, I wholeheartedly concur. Having presented the opinions of many others in this lecture, the following represents my own position:

1. The big bang represents an immensely powerful, yet carefully controlled, release of matter, energy, space, and time within the strict confines of very carefully fine-tuned physical constants and laws that govern their behavior and interactions. The power and care this explosion reveals exceed human potential for design by multiple orders of magnitude.

2. A Creator must exist. The big bang ripples (April, 1992) and subsequent scientific findings are clearly pointing to an ex nihilo creation consistent with the first few verses of the book of Genesis.

3. The Creator must have awesome power and wisdom. The quantity of material and the power resources within our universe are truly immense. The information, or intricacy, manifest in any part of the universe, and (as Allan Sandage has well stated) especially in a living organism, is beyond our ability to comprehend. And what we do see is only what God has shown us within our four dimensions of space and time!

4. The Creator is loving. The simplicity, balance, order, elegance, and beauty seen throughout the creation demonstrate that God is loving rather than capricious. Further, the capacity and desire to nurture and to protect, seen in so many creatures, makes sense if their Creator possesses these same attributes. It is apparent that God cares for His creatures, for He has provided for their needs.

5. The Creator is just and requires justice. Inward reflection and outward investigation affirm that human beings have a conscience. The conscience reflects the reality of right and wrong and the necessity of obedience.

6. Each of us falls hopelessly short of the Creator's standard. We incur His displeasure when we violate any part of God's moral law in our actions, our words, and our thoughts. Who can keep his or her thoughts and attitudes pure for even an hour? Certainly not me. If each person falls short of his or her own standards, how much more so of God's perfect standards? For many years I sought to get a "passing grade" with God by comparing myself with other sinners.

7. Because the Creator is loving, wise, and powerful, He made a way to rescue us. When we come to a point of concern about our personal failings, we can begin to understand from the creation around us that God's love, wisdom, and power are sufficient to deliver us from our otherwise hopeless situation.

If we trust our lives totally to the Rescuer, Jesus Christ, we will be saved. The one and only path is to give up all human attempts to satisfy God's requirements and put our trust solely in Jesus Christ and in His chosen means of redemption, namely, His death on the cross.

[1] This essay has not been published to date, but will be forthcoming in a book by Dr. Henry F. Schaefer. In that book, there is a chapter entitled "The Ten Questions that Intellectuals Ask about Christianity." Several of these questions arise persistently during Q&A sessions after the lecture on cosmology presented in this essay.

[2] Ross, Hugh. *The Fingerprint of God* (Pittsburgh, PA: Whitaker House. 2nd Edition, 1989): 3.

[3] Ibid., 58-59.

[4] Jammer, Max. *Einstein and Religion* (Princeton: Princeton University Press, 1999): 241.

[5] Ross, *The Fingerprint of God*, 17.

[6] Dicke, R. H., Peebles, P. J. E., Roll, P. G., and Wilkinson, D. T. "*Cosmic Black-Body Radiation*", *Astrophysical Journal*. 142 (1965): 415.

[7] Bartlett, J.G., A. Blanchard, J. Silk, M.S. Turner. "The Case for a Hubble Constant of 30 km/s/Mpc." *Science*. 267, 17 February (1995): 980.

[8] Browne, Malcolm. "Clues to the Universe's Origin Expected." *New York Times*, 12 March 1978, p. 1, col. 54.

[9] Brian, Denis. *Genius Talk* (New York: Plenum Publishing, 1995): 153-177.

[10] Hawking, Stephen. *A Brief History of Time: A Reader's Companion*, edited by Gene Stone (London: Bantam Books, 1993): 63.

[11] Maugh, Thomas H. "Relics of 'Big Bang' Seen for First Time," *Los Angeles Times*, 24 April 1992, A1 and A30.

[12] Smoot, George, and Keay Davidson. *Wrinkles in Time* (New York: William Morrow & Co., 1993): 283.

[13] Briggs, David. "Science, Religion, Are Discovering Commonality in Big Bang Theory," *Los Angeles Times*, 2 May 1992, 86-87.

[14] Strauss, Stephen. "An Innocent's Guide to Big Bang Theory: Fingerprint in Space Left by the Universe as a Baby Still Has Doubters Hurling Stones," *The Globe and Mail* (Toronto), 25 April 1992, 1.

[15] Smoot and Davidson, *Wrinkles in Time*, 17.

[16] Ross, Hugh. *Creator and the Cosmos* (Third Edition, Colorado Springs, CO: NavPress, 2001): 108.

[17] Gleiser, Marcello. *The Dancing Universe* (New York: Dutton Publishing, 1997): 303.

[18] Lederman, Leon. *The God Particle* (New York: Dell Publishing, 1993).

[19] Hawking, *A Reader's Companion*.

[20] Guth, Alan. *The Inflationary Universe: The Quest for a New Theory of Cosmic Origins* (Cambridge, MA: Perseus Publishing, 1998).

[21] Hawking, Stephen. *A Brief History of Time: The Updated and Expanded Tenth Anniversary Edition* (New York: Bantam Books, 1996).

[22] Lewis, C.S. *That Hideous Strength* (New York: Scribner Publishers, 1996).

[23] Morris, Errol (Director). *A Brief History of Time*, Paramount Communications, 1992.

[24] Hawking, *A Reader's Companion*, 63.

[25] Hartle, James and Stephen Hawking. "Wave Function of the Universe", *Physical Review* D. 28, 2960 (1983).

[26] White, Michael and John Gribbon. *Stephen Hawking: Life in Science* (New York: Viking Penguin 1992).

[27] Ibid., 63, 70.

[28] Hawking, *A Reader's Companion*, 54.

[29] BBC Television Broadcast. *Master of the Universe* (1989).

[30] ABC Television Broadcast. 20/20 (1989).

[31] Hawking, *Updated and Expanded Edition*, 190.

[32] Ibid., 183.

[33] Ibid., 122.

[34] Hawking, Stephen. "Letters to the Editor," *American Scientist*. 73 (1985): 12.

[35] Hawking, *Updated and Expanded Edition*, 146.

[36] Calvin, John. This comment is widely attributed to Calvin, but without reference.

[37] Ross, *Creator and the Cosmos*, 108.

[38] Greenstein, George. *The Symbiotic Universe* (New York: William Morrow, 1988): 27.

[39] Weinberg, Steven. *Dreams of a Final Theory* (New York: Patheon Books, 1992).

[40] Dyson, Freeman. "Energy in the Universe," *Scientific American*. 225, No. 3, (September 1971): 50-59.

[41] Rees, Martin. Cited by Hugh Ross in Ross' book, *Creator and the Cosmos*, 158.

[42] Davies, Paul. *The Cosmic Blueprint* (New York: Simon & Schuster, 1989).

[43] Craig, William Lane. *British Journal of Philosophy and Science* 38 (1988): 392.

[44] Hawking, *Updated and Expanded Edition*, 144.

[45] Ibid.

[46] White and Gribbon, 166.

[47] Guth, Alan. "The Impossibility of a Bouncing Universe", *Nature*. 302 (1983): 505.

[48] Rees, Martin. *Just Six Numbers* (New York: Basic Books, 2002).

[49] Polkinghorne, John. *Quarks, Chaos and Christianity* (New York: Crossroad Publishing Co., 1996): 32.

[50] Holder, Rodney. *Science & Christian Belief*. 13 (April 2001): 5-24.

[51] Boberg, Carl G. "How Great Thou Art" hymn (1885).

[52] Lightman, Alan. *Origins: The Lives and Worlds of Modern Cosmologists* (Cambridge, MA: Harvard University Press, 1990).

[53] Larson, Edward. *Nature*. 394 (1998): 313.

[54] Townes, Charles. *Making Waves* (American Physical Society, 1995). Also cited in Margenau, Henry, and Roy Varghese, *Cosmos, Bios, Theos* (LaSalle, IL: Open Court Publishing, 1992): 123.

[55] Margenau, Henry, and Roy Varghese. *Cosmos, Bios, Theos* (LaSalle, IL: Open Court Publishing, 1992): 107.

[56] Ibid., 88.

[57] Panek, Richard. " The Loneliness of the Long Distance Cosmologist" *New York Times*, 25 July 1999, Section 6, p. 22, col. 1.

[58] Lightman, Alan. *Origins: The Lives and Worlds of Modern Cosmologists* (Cambridge, MA: Harvard University Press, 1990).

[59] Sandage, Allan. "A Scientist Reflects on Religious Belief", *Truth*. 1(1985): 54.

[60] Ellis, George. "Quantum Cosmology and the Laws of Nature" (*Vatican Observatory*, 1993): 378.

[61] Hawking, *A Reader's Companion*, 111.

[62] Ibid.

[63] Ibid.

[64] Isham, Chris

[65] Schrödinger, Erwin. *What is Life?* (1942) (republished by Cambridge, UK: Cambridge University Press, 1992).

[66] Schrödinger, Erwin. *Nature and the Greeks* (Cambridge, UK: Cambridge University Press, 1954).

[67] BBC Television Broadcast. *Master of the Universe* (1989).

[68] Johnson, Phillip. *Reason in the Balance* (Downers Grove, IL: InterVarsity Press, 1995): 226.

[69] Feynman, Richard. *The Character of Physical Law* (New York: Random House, 1994).

[70] Ross, *The Fingerprint of God*, 181-182.

Part II:

Naturalism in Science

Chapter Three

—◦∿∿◦—

IS SCIENTIFIC NATURALISM
SCIENTIFIC?

WITH AUDIENCE DISCUSSION

Phillip Johnson

Phillip Johnson is the Jefferson E. Peyser Professor of Law, Emeritus at the University of California at Berkeley and has been on the law faculty there since 1968. He authored two law school casebooks and wrote several best-selling books on science, philosophy and religion, including Darwin on Trial, Reason in the Balance: The Case Against Naturalism in Science, Law, and Education, and The Right Questions: Truth, Meaning, and Public Debate. Professor Johnson also served as Associate Dean at UC, Berkeley for three years and has expertise on a wide variety of law subjects, including criminal law, criminal procedure, and contemporary legal theory and has served as a law clerk in both the California Supreme Court and the U.S. Supreme Court.

Abstract

Scientific naturalism insists that nature is all there is, or at least the only thing about which we can have any knowledge. It follows that nature had to do its own creating, which does not include any role for God. We are not supposed to approach this philosophy with open-minded skepticism, but to believe it on faith. But, if we take evolution away from the worldview-promoters and return it to the real scientific investigators, a chronic social conflict will become an exciting intellectual adventure.

My Personal Story

I GREW UP IN A NOMINALLY CHRISTIAN FAMILY in the Midwest. When I went to Harvard University, I went with the intention of accepting the value system and the ways of thinking there. As far as I was concerned, Harvard was the number one university in the United States or the world and that was why I wanted to study there.

In chapter one of my book, *The Wedge of Truth* [1], I relate the story of a young man named Philip Wentworth, who went to Harvard in 1924. He professed to have lost his Christian faith there unexpectedly when confronted with new ideas. However, the undertones of Wentworth's writings suggest that he went there – just as I did – with the intention of losing it all. Long before that crisis of faith, even before leaving home, he made up his mind to do so. This was a natural thing for an ambitious young person to do. Like a young Catholic seminarian going to Rome to study, I went to the "secular intellectual city" called Harvard University.

I believed then that the highest goal was to become a big shot in one way or another—in Washington, the Supreme Court, academia, business, or another field. My particular interests led me into law school, where I did well enough to become something of an academic big shot. From a clerkship at the U.S. Supreme Court, I landed a faculty position at the University of California at Berkeley at the age of 27, having punched my ticket in the right places and having prepared for that kind of success. [2]

During this time, I had left behind the outdated, old-fashioned aspects of my religious upbringing. However, I was never the kind of agnostic who was passionately hostile to Christianity. Ironically, my first wife was passionately anti-Christian, but she had been raised in a religiously conservative family and had rebelled against it.

I regretfully lamented, "It's too bad we really can't believe those things anymore." I read all of C. S. Lewis' popular books and appreciated them, but they didn't seem for a person of my time and place. I managed to rationalize a convenient belief system that was reinforced by my surrounding culture and flattered myself into thinking I had somehow found truth through my own power of reason.

Disillusionment

My life went along rather well until in my late thirties, when I went through a typical professor's midlife crisis. The extremes of radical feminism in the 1970s cut through many marriages and mine was no exception. At age 37, I found myself a divorced single parent who was somewhat disillusioned with the academic legal career I was pursuing. I continued to get the requisite promotions, tenure, and so forth, but it seemed to me that academic work had wasted my talent and kept me from doing something worthwhile for a career. I became disillusioned by the measures of success I had entertained in my married life, family life, and professional life.

I heard the gospel and I had two thoughts. ... My earlier belief that I had a more advanced way of thinking suddenly became less appealing, even absurd.

There was a moment of crisis the very day my first marriage broke up. I went with my 11-year-old daughter to a Vacation Bible School she was attending with a neighbor. I went to church that night knowing I was going to tell my daughter afterward that her mother was moving out to live somewhere else. In this heightened state of awareness, I heard the gospel – nothing was particularly distinctive about the delivery, nor was it more persuasive than I had heard prior to this occasion. But, I had two thoughts. *First*, I thought this person actually believes what he is saying and lives by it. That is the most effective kind of message. *Second*, there is no reason I couldn't do that, too. My earlier belief that I had a more advanced way of thinking suddenly became less appealing, even absurd. It was proof of my self-delusion.

A Christian in the University

I became a Christian in my late thirties, as an "already established professor." I am frequently asked: "Don't they try to get rid of you at Berkeley?' and "Doesn't the school consider you an embarrassment?" One reporter even asked me: "When you come into the faculty club, do the other professors turn their backs?" Actually, I preside at the center table since I was already established when these events unfolded. Berkeley simply had to accept me on my terms. It really is a very tolerant place in that sense.

I soon became a member of First Presbyterian Church of Berkeley, where I met my second wife, Kathie, and where I grew more involved in the Christian life. The church was almost next door to UC, Berkeley, an institution that historically prides itself as the world's greatest scientific institution. Although Earl Palmer, our pastor, was also the chaplain for the Cal Bears football team and faculty members sat in neighboring pews, there prevailed a general assumption that we in the church and the University community only blocks away were in a harmonious relationship. I instinctively knew that this was not true.

"We don't have to deal with the religious questions any more. They're off the table. If God did exist, He'd just be part of nature, too."

Professor John Searle, *Philosophy, UCal, Berkeley*

I understood the faculty mindset from the inside, so I knew that few of my colleagues were aware that First Presbyterian Church of Berkeley even existed. To them, Christianity was regarded as something akin to a cult and it was assumed that those who took Christian faith seriously, literally, or as a statement about reality were hopelessly ignorant. Thus, when the assertion was made in church, "In the beginning was the Word," as a true statement about the nature of reality, it was clear to me that this concrete proposition was not believed at all in the university community. There was no need for any explicit statement of disbelief; it was just taken for granted.

My colleague, John Searle, summarized that mindset by saying, "We don't have to deal with the religious questions any more. They're off the table. If God did exist, He'd just be part of nature, too." In other words, it was inconceivable that there could be valid reality outside of the natural. As William Provine (professor of evolutionary biology at Cornell University, and my friendly adversary in numerous debates) states, "If you've read Darwin and go to church, you're throwing your brains out the window to do it."

Understanding the Conflict

As I considered different worldviews, it was clear to me that this was not a superficial conflict. Some might protest: "There is not a real conflict. Some people just don't understand that evolution may have been God's method of creating. After all, couldn't God have used natural selection?" This is superficial thinking and a theological "straw man" that can be easily defeated. Of course, God can do anything; after all, that is the very definition of his omnipotence. When the question is asked, "Isn't it possible that God could have ...?" it seems to be the world's most boring question. My customary response is: "Stop. The answer is yes."

All intelligent people are not agnostics, but the dominant intellectual forces certainly are—and that is the heart of the problem.

This speculation is alien to the university milieu since the methodology of the scientific study of evolution is based on a naturalistic understanding of reality-nature is all there is, therefore nature had to do its own creating. In this paradigm, God is merely a projection of the human mind. That was a dangerous thought in the nineteenth century when it was first proposed, but it is a common assumption in the academy today. I wanted to resolve the fundamental conflict between the naturalistic thinking taken for granted, not just in scientific departments but throughout the university and Christian thinking.

I like to ask Christian audiences, "If the gospel is true, why are all intelligent people agnostics?" Of course, this is exaggeration designed to provoke, though with a kernel of truth. All intelligent people are not agnostics, but the dominant intellectual forces certainly are—and that is the heart of the problem.

I was impressed by a small conference for a half-dozen "out-of-the-closet" Christian professors. Each was asked what difference being a Christian made in his or her life as a professor. One by one, they answered, "I'm nice to students." "I keep longer office hours." "I worry about their personal problems." These were very decent things and they were very decent people, but none addressed the intellectual substance of their work. When engineering professors (as most of them were) made this sort of remark, that was okay, since it was not clear how a Christian would do engineering differently as a substantive activity. However, when an English professor got up and said, "I wouldn't bring my faith into the classroom, because it wouldn't be relevant to anything intellectual," I was shocked and replied, "This field is ideological from top to bottom. How can this possibly be the case?"

A Year in England

Those ideas filled my head as I departed for England on sabbatical leave for the 1987-88 academic year—the year that would change my life. I lived in London and had a nice office at the University College Faculty of Law, but had no teaching duties, plans or clear-cut project to do. I told the university I was going to study insurance law, and if I had in fact done that, I would be a very rich man by now. Had I not been a metaphysical naturalist, epistemological relativist, and agnostic, I would have concluded that divine Providence had me walk past London's leading scientific bookstore on the way to my office each day. In the bookstore window, I saw Richard Dawkins' *The Blind Watchmaker* and Michael Denton's *Evolution: A Theory in Crisis.* As I picked up a different book every day, I grew fascinated with the subject and began to delve into the professional literature.

What was the appeal of this subject? First, in reading about the evolution controversy, I realized the controversy was being fundamentally misrepresented by the secular scientific community and therefore misunderstood by the public. The confrontation between evolution and creation was commonly depicted as a conflict over the details and chronology of the creation process, or as a squabble between Genesis literalists, on the one hand, and scientific investigators on the other: Do you open your mind to "the facts" like a good scientist, or do you stick with the primitive biblical account as a fundamentalist would?" Richard Dawkins had the question right, but the wrong answer. Dawkins honed in on what the evolutionary story is really all about: "How can you get the creation of these wondrously complex things we call living "organisms started without God having any part in it?"

That was the issue that shaped the fundamental question of the debate: "Can the creating be done without a Creator or not?"

Dawkins did not minimize the problem. He pointed out that biology is the study of complex things that look as if a Creator designed them for a purpose. Each cell contains more information than all the volumes of the *Encyclopedia Britannica* combined. Dawkins asserted that Darwin, and contemporary versions of evolutionary theory, had successfully shown that this could be done by nature alone without the need for a Creator. That was the issue that shaped the fundamental question of the debate: "Can the creating be done without a Creator or not?"

That's the fundamental question. This is dealing with something much more profound than whether one reads Genesis literally or whether one reads Genesis by any method or even reads it at all. The basic question of theism is the same: "Must a Creator to do the creating or can nature do it without the Creator?"

The Issue of Rhetoric

Reading Dawkins carefully for a second time, I saw that he carried the argument with bluff, with shifting definitions, and with his ability to "hide the pea under a different shell." He never succeeded in demonstrating or presenting any convincing evidence for the creative power of the alternative creation mechanism that he proposed. In fact,

I recognized his maneuvering as the kind of thing I knew backwards and forwards from my lifelong study of legal argument. There is a species of flim-flam that is done in legal argument all the time, assuming the answer in the way the question is stated; it is a form of "hiding the ball," of misdirecting attention, the verbal equivalent of a magician's tricks. I had lifelong training in spotting this sort of thing and countering it.

This perspective will help to answer the question so many ask me: Why would a law professor take up this scientific topic? The answer is that it is not, in fact, a scientific topic, but a question of how rhetoric is used to accomplish a philosophical objective. After all, the science is extremely simple, as witnessed by the books that present Darwinism to the general public. (As an aside, I have often found the popular books far more informative about the substantive issues of creation and naturalism than the professional literature, where the important issues tend to be implicit and simply assumed. Furthermore, the "popular" sources do not necessarily suffer from low quality or lack of authority. The major figures in evolutionary biology—from pioneers like Darwin and Huxley to contemporaries like Gould and Dawkins—all directed their arguments to the general public.

Apart from rhetoric, I saw that different authorities (e.g., Gould and Dawkins) who actually disagreed over all the significant points nonetheless closed ranks when faced with a challenge from outside for instance, from the creationists, whom they defined as narrow-minded biblical literalists. They indiscriminately lumped under the same "fundamentalist-creationist" term anyone who believed in God and put any credence in that belief system. However, in recent opinion polls, the term is broad enough to include 90% of the American public as unacceptably theistic and supernatural. This insight was my most crucial realization. I said to myself, "My gosh, so this is where the bodies are buried!" The great triumph of naturalistic thinking was the explication of our creation story. That function of the naturalist 'story' explained why it was so important and so crucial to protect from criticism.

The Necessary Creation Story

Every culture necessarily has a creation story, or cosmogony, which provides the foundation for knowledge of every kind. The creation story answers a host of other questions: How do individuals fit into ultimate reality? What are trustworthy sources of information? If you were created by a Creator who cares about your existence, you would look for revelation from that Creator and seek to establish a right relationship with that Creator. However, if that schema is exposed as a myth and you are told the Creator is not real, you pursue a different course in life, value different sources of information, and pursue different goals. After all, it would be folly to seek a right relationship with a fictitious Creator who is merely the product of your own mind.

After all, it would be folly to seek a right relationship with a fictitious Creator who is merely the product of your own mind.

One particular version of the creation story that is currently fashionable is one I characterize as "materialist mythology." It states that unassisted matter operating only with chance, change, and the principle of natural selection can and did accomplish the creation of biological organisms in all their present complexity and diversity. Part of the cover for this creation story is that it appears to originate in unbiased, scientific investigation, and—so the argument goes—is opposed only by those who willfully shut their eyes to the obvious evidence presented to them and insist on sticking to the Genesis story. But, the reverse actually is true. While science dominates religion today, the religion of science is, in fact, the materialist myth. The view that "nature is our creator" exercises as compelling an effect on the interpretation of scientific evidence as any form of religion ever did.

In November 1987, I was in London and said to my wife, Kathie, "I have finally figured this out. I know what's wrong and I think I know what to do about it. But, I am too intelligent to adopt this as a professional goal because it would consume my life and be a never-ending battle. I would be attacked on all sides. People would criticize me and say, 'What are your qualifications to say these things?' No rational person would want to risk their professional reputation, but the next morning I began this irresistible challenge and have never looked back.

Biology and Logic

As a legal scholar approaching and mastering this subject, I recognize that Dawkins and Gould, like most biologists, are not trained to recognize hidden assumptions—or even to think logically. Rather, they are trained to accept the thinking of the other people in their department, laboratory, and discipline. A biologist faced with a pure logical contradiction will simply shrug if that contradiction is well accepted in the field.

Notice that my thesis is *not* that individual biologists cannot think logically, but rather, that, if they do think logically, this occurs in spite of their professional training at the doctoral level. The field as a whole is not one that embraces the thought: "Let's think about what is commonly accepted and what might be wrong with it." I have certainly not observed that approach at Berkeley or elsewhere. Of course, the legal mind goes to the other extreme of incessant questioning. Nonetheless, the particular logic of legal analysis seemed especially appropriate to this area of inquiry.

I also hoped to bring to this conflict a sense of strategy. From the standpoint of the Christian world, the evolution fight has been a losing battle in which few wish to become entangled. On the one hand, there are the adherents of creation science and the defenders of Genesis. They have achieved a constituency of millions and made a considerable impact, but they have been intellectually marginalized and limited to the fundamentalist subculture. They have been ridiculed and lack any visible success in bringing their viewpoint or ideas to the general culture.

Even in Christian academic or intellectual circles, and within most denominations, one senses that it is embarrassing to take up this issue since it frequently brings the faith into disrepute. Rather than embarking on a war with science, it is more productive simply to accept the reign of naturalism and work within it the best you can. A common response is: "Evolution is God's way of creating. Now, let's change the subject and go on to something else." No one wants to be identified with a losing cause.

Redefining the Debate

In essence, my project was to take a "loser" and turn it into a "winner" and I had no doubt it could be done. There was clearly a constituency of enormous scope to which we could appeal. Gallup polls consistently showed about 44% (or nearly half) of the public are outright creationists. Another large sector of the public views evolution as God's intended way of creating human beings. In theistic evolution, they find a reconciliation of science and religion which they can accept. However, they are wrong on all scores.

Whether the "hard-core" or "soft-core" version of creationism is at issue, the creation story appeals to nearly 90% of the U.S. population.

God-guided evolution contradicts classical evolutionary thought almost as much as does outright creationism. The nature of scientific evolutionary thinking is that, by definition, it provides an explanation of how creating is accomplished without any supernatural influence. Any overseeing intelligence would represent a supernatural, non-evolved mind, which the closed reasoning of evolution makes ineligible as a "first cause." This contradiction of theistic evolutionism shows that God-guided evolution is not actually evolution at all, in the scientific sense of the term – it is slow creation (or I call it "soft-core creationism"). Whether the "hard-core" or "soft-core" version of creationism is at issue, the creation story appeals to nearly 90% of the U.S. population.

The trick, as I saw it, was to redefine the question being debated in such a manner as to accomplish two goals. First, the issue should be debatable in the mainstream intellectual and academic communities, unlike the previous "Bible *versus* science" polarity. Furthermore, the question should be framed in such a way that it reflects the kind of thinking already existing within postmodern academia. That line of discussion would involve the exposure of "hidden assumptions" and the question of whether claims of objective knowledge are in fact contingent upon subject values, since many claims of objective knowledge are in fact subjective value claims smuggled in as scientific fact. Asking the right question is crucial and many postmodernists correctly raise this key question—a contribution we can accept without "eating the whole enchilada" of total relativization.

Our framing of the issue follows this line of argument—there are two definitions of science in our culture. On one hand, science is objective evaluation of the facts and scientists follow the facts without prejudice wherever they lead. On the other hand, science is a naturalistic philosophy that attempts to explain all phenomena in natural terms. This definition emerges explicitly in discussions of the scientific method and in the insistence that everything be a product of natural causes. For example, regardless of the evidence, the emergence of life must be the product of purely natural forces in which God played no part.

You are forbidden to ask the open question: "Can non-living chemicals spontaneously come together to form a life form?" The typical response to that "outside-the-box" query would be, "That is not an appropriate question. However, if you must ask, the answer is that it must have happened at least once." The proof of that *statement of faith* is, "Life exists." or, "Life was, is, and always will be." If we ask, "Is there an alternative that God created it?" the answer is, "That transgresses the boundaries of science and moves into religion. However, science is committed to explanations based on natural causes.

If the evidence points to an intelligent cause—to a Creator outside of nature—do we follow the evidence or the philosophy? This is the key issue to debate.

If the evidence points to an intelligent cause—to a Creator outside of nature, do we follow the evidence—or the philosophy? This is the key issue to debate. Notice the Bible is not mentioned here. We only challenge the "sacred cow" that is never challenged, employing intellectual arguments against it that are standard in other subjects in the university. This is the first goal.

Uniting the People of God

The second goal, which involves the religious side of the debate, is to frame the one issue that unites, rather than divide, the people of God. The issue of the Genesis chronology divides. It divides Catholic from Protestant, young-earth from old-earth, religious Jews from Christians. Scientific naturalists put much effort into keeping it that way. It is certainly to their advantage to keep those who are religious divided over it so they advance the stereotype of narrow-minded fundamentalists.

If the central issue is highlighted—that is, "Must a Creator exist, or did nature create itself?"—there is support from all the religious groups since they all agree on the reality of a Creator.

But, if the central issue is highlighted—that is, "Must a Creator exist, or did nature create itself? —there is support from all the religious groups since they all agree on the reality of a Creator. It may require more education and coaching to convey the importance of focusing on this unifying issue, but these diverse groups will eventually see it is unquestionably in their interest to agree on this particular issue. This is now a movement that avoids the divisive issues and deals with the central, and most important, issue. Incidentally, this issue is the one where the evolutionary naturalists are most vulnerable. The intelligent design movement displays ecumenism, from the Catholic, Michael Behe, to the Eastern Orthodox convert, John Mark Reynolds, and secular Jew, David Berlinsky, and some other heterodox types as well. The key is to build a movement centered on a simple, general concept, not a parochial, or restrictive, creed or faith statement that might be more appropriate for a denominational college. We must achieve a broad-based agreement that this issue deserves to be on the table.

Conclusion:
Asking the Right Questions

Real intellectual power consists not in prescribing the answers, but in getting the right questions on the table. I am not worried about what people think are the ultimate answers. If somebody says to me: "I want to put forth this issue on the table: Can natural forces do the creating, and can they create genetic information? I am an atheistic materialist and I think we can prove it. Darwinism has its troubles, but we'll come up with a better scheme, then we'll defeat you religious people." To this, I say: "There stands an ally."

It cannot be overstated that real intellectual power consists not in prescribing the answers, but in getting the right questions on the table.

William Provine, Michael Ruse, and others who have agreed to debate us at crucial points are, in this regard, associate members of the movement. While they differ from us on the answers, they recognize that we raise the right questions and there is agreement to level the playing field in order to give truth a chance to speak for itself—which it always will. As the apostle Paul instructs the fledgling Roman church, the truth is suppressed in unrighteousness. That is what keeps idolatry and false theoretical systems going. We simply need not overpower people with arguments.

When I debate a major figure in the scientific world, my goal is not to embarrass my opponent, who then goes away muttering: "Johnson is a clever lawyer who knows the best arguments." I far prefer that an audience and my opponent go away saying: "That was more interesting than I expected. We must do this again. We must keep this discussion going and keep this issue on the table." And if they say as well, "I think somebody else could do a better job arguing for it than Johnson," so much the better. It is the cause that needs to win, not the advocate. That is my goal as well – to let the truth speak for itself.

Audience Discussion[3]

Q1:   You have dealt primarily with evolution. On the origin of the universe issues, are some of the same issues at stake there? Are physicists actually asking questions more honestly?

Bob Kaita, a physicist from Princeton University, is in the audience and he can speak to that.

Bob: In *A Brief History of Time*, Stephen Hawking actually says the "agenda" is to find one theory of everything, for then you rid yourself of the need for God. God is then unnecessary. In following what Phil said, I would not call Hawking an "ally," but he clearly puts his agenda on the table.   There are also people in the physical sciences who are outspoken advocates of our position.

Phil: I agree with Bob. He's referring to the point that Hawking refutes, by getting to a single theory of everything, the "fine tuning argument," that there have to be so many different constants that are "just so," somebody had to set the constants and that points to a creator.

The scientific rationalist would like to eliminate that kind of messiness and say, "There wasn't any 'fine tuning' done because there was only one way for everything to be done. There was no choice in the matter." This is one way to eliminate God. It is false to ever say science is independent of religion and that scientists are doing some science with nothing to do with religion. You see they can't write a book without putting God in the title. The Hawking trademark line is, "We shall know the mind of God." He says that in every interview and it is obvious that this is a fundamentally religious project.

It seems the cosmologists, the physicists, who do this tend not to be "hard core" materialists like the evolutionary biologists and molecular biologists, like Francis Crick for example. They tend toward a Platonism, because to them it's not the particles that are fundamental. It's the laws. The final theory is the object of worship. It's the mathematical relationship. That's kind of like a Platonic ideal. It makes them tend toward a sort of pantheism as the natural process.

The scientific world, the agnostic world, the university world can live with a God who creates at the ultimate beginning and then steps aside. They don't like it, but they can live with it so long as everything after the big bang is the product of unbroken chance and law. Then God is so distant that you can forget about him, but a God who is active in the life processes is quite another matter. That's why it's very different level of intensity when you get involved there.

Since the big Big Bang came up, I will share my own thinking. A great many theists embrace the big Big Bang enthusiastically; even build theologies on it, because it's a creation moment. I can appreciate that. I am not disputing what they say, but I have a little different slant on it. What concerns about the big bang is the many *ad hoc* assumptions, inflation and so on, that are used to explain difficulties.

The interesting question is, "From where did the information come?" That's the question biology aspires to answer.

The Big Bang is a story about how matter comes into existence and is distributed around the universe. To me, that is not the most interesting question. The interesting question is, "From where did the information come?" That's the question biology aspires to answer. Any scientific answer that doesn't explain how we get an information-rich universe isn't dealing with the most important question of origins. My objection to the big bang is that it really doesn't address the important part of creation, the "where did the information come from" issue.

Q2: Even if the critics of Darwinism and materialism are right, how can we expect to see our vast scientific enterprise ever change?

It's a subject that fascinates me. I've been asked by a lot of scientific audiences, "Just look at the implausibility of what you are saying. You are a professor of law and you haven't taken biology since high school and you tell us this world of brilliant scientific observers made a fundamental mistake and got the most important part of science all wrong? How can this ever be the case?"

It does seem implausible, but I have combed the literature and I know they don't have an answer to the question of how information was created. They have many other difficulties I have written about in my books.

In looking back to the 19th century, the fossil experts gave Darwin fits. They were his main enemies, because they said the fossil record did not fit his theory. The clergy gave in almost immediately—and I am speaking here of seminary professors, bishops of the Church of England, and so on. There was minimal opposition and Darwin was buried with full honors in Westminster Abbey. People could challenge the details, but not the way of thinking. My colleague, Steven Meyer, and I call it "The Enchantment."

In the United States, there were two major intellectual opponents of Darwinism. One was Louis Agassiz, Professor of Natural History at Harvard. Ironically, when Agassiz said, "Darwinism is false. It doesn't fit the evidence," he lost his scientific reputation almost overnight. The other opponent of Darwinism was Charles Hodge, the foremost Presbyterian theologian of the time. He gave in to scientific pressure and finally said he understood the Darwinian mechanism. He got the main issue right when he stated that, "Darwinism is atheism." It might be more accurate to say "Naturalism is atheism," but either way, it cost Hodge his reputation as well.

There were reasons they wanted to believe Darwinism. It freed them from biblical morality and church institutions—and seemed to set in motion a perception of unlimited scientific advance. This dream is still with us.

After a century of enlightenment rationalism, the philosophies of Voltaire, Thomas Paine, Thomas Jefferson. David Hume, and Kant "set the stage" for a naturalistic understanding of reality. Their motive was formed by many things, but Christianity was ripe for this type of attack. It had been held responsible for centuries of religious war and oppression, and with some justification. Therefore, it was perceived as a bad thing rather than a good thing. Since the churches aligned themselves with the feudal system and monarchies, this age of political democracy became an age that challenged the churches.

There were reasons they wanted to believe Darwinism. It freed them from biblical morality and church institutions—and seemed to set in motion a perception of unlimited scientific advance. This dream is still with us.

You read the visionaries of science in the popular literature today and they make grandiose claims like, "If we sequence the human genome, we'll conquer all disease and make better people because we can reprogram DNA." Computer scientists make grandiose claims like, "We will figure out the information, download it into a computer, and give people eternal life." Books by Ray Kurzweil and others promote the idea that science can ultimately produce spiritual machines. We need not conquer the universe because science can create a better virtual reality. This dream is religious and energizes the whole system. That is why the Darwinian system was accepted rapidly in the academy and all dissent was driven out.

Q3: You used the term "naturalistic thinking." What do you mean by that?

Naturalism is the doctrine that nature is all there is. I call it epistemological naturalism. That is the case made by the Christian philosopher, Alvin Plantinga, one of the world's most prominent philosophers, when he challenges epistemological naturalism.

You can't have God-guided evolution because it wouldn't be evolution at all in the scientific sense. Evolution must be a mindless product.

There is no such thing as guided evolution. You can't have God-guided evolution because it wouldn't be evolution at all in the scientific sense. Evolution must be a mindless product. You cannot have a mind to guide it until mind evolves mindlessly from "non-mind." That is the doctrine.

This is what I think you are asking. A materialistic or naturalistic understanding of reality explains everything in terms of chance and law, including the thoughts in your brain. Francis Crick, the famous biochemist who co-discovered the structure of DNA, wrote in the opening statement in his book, *The Astonishing Hypothesis,*

> The astonishing hypothesis is this, dear reader, what if your thoughts are nothing but the product of neurons firing mindlessly in your brain? Then, we can explain the cause of your thoughts. But, your thoughts have no independent, objective truth to them, because they're just products of this mindless system.[4]

This is one of the fundamental contradictions of the whole materialistic process and they cannot face it. This is why I conclude that it is false to think that theism, especially Christian theism, is antithetical to scientific thinking. It is the basis of scientific thinking. The necessary and metaphysical basis is that our minds are created in the image of the creator's mind. That's why we can understand how things really are—to a point.

Here is where you need the rest of Christian theology. Why can't we understand things better than we do? Why do we go off on self-deceptive projects like Darwinism? I believe it is because our minds are not in a right relationship to the creator, the Logos that was in the beginning. That's the basis of the human predicament.

So this metaphysical story, aside from its Biblical roots, is a necessary background to scientific and rational accomplishment of every kind, and materialism deconstructs the mind. These things never last forever. When C.S. Lewis wrote in the mid-20th century, it was at flood tide. While he pointed out some of the problems and did quite well, he never took on this battle, nor should he have. It wasn't his gift, and the time wasn't right for it.

That's when the Miller Uri experiment was done and they thought they had found the preconditions for the origin of life by chemical evolution. Neo-Darwinism was new and seemed to hold unlimited promise. At a time like that, they can say, "Even if we haven't solved everything yet, we've made so many great discoveries." But now, they are running out of gas and we can begin to expose some contradictions. But, back to your original question – yes, you are right, naturalistic thinking is not thinking at all.

Q4: Our university has hard-core evolutionists who say, "It's just a matter of time."

Yes, they don't give up on that easily. Of course, there are people at every university who will say things like that. Now, there are different ways of responding to that claim and they are rather persuasive. But, the claim of needing more time would not have been as persuasive 50 years ago.

Evolution is losing ground in terms of the basic scientific claims, particularly about the mechanism. The main question is how you get the creating done without a mind to direct it.

Evolution is running out of steam and losing ground in terms of the basic scientific claims, particularly about the mechanism. They still find fossils here and there, but the main question is how you get the creating done without a mind to direct it.

Q5: After reviewing many papers to see how evolution was introduced, I felt it was often gratuitously included. The author could have substituted creation, or nothing at all, and little would have changed in the papers. Can you comment on this?

That is often what occurs in the academic world in biological sciences and public television. Public television programs may be about fish doing wondrous things, but the underlying message implies, "Evolution did this. Isn't evolution wonderful?" Very rarely is any detail given about how evolution did what it supposedly did because there is neither an accessible history nor a testable process that can describe how these things were created. There is clearly great effort to sell the idea that evolution did the creating.

After speaking to someone who studied molecular biology at MIT, I realized he never took a course in evolution nor a course that examined the evidence. Evolution was just "assumed" as the basis for everything they studied. It was "assumed" the world was a closed system of material causes and effects which cannot be influenced by anything outside it—especially a Creator. You are told the Creator only exists in your imagination and the presupposition of this teaching is that only "unintelligent material processes" really happen. This is what is meant by evolution.

So, I agree with the point you made in your question. This issue is often raised in a gratuitous way. For example, in the west region of the National Park Service (NPS), I heard of an administrator who requires NPS guides to emphasize evolution in their public tours. In fact, guides are fired if they don't believe it fervently enough. Therefore, it is not just in the universities, but also in many areas of society. The Creator never seems to get "credit."

Q6: Are Christians in academia a dying breed?

No, I don't think so. I see the glass as half full. It is just remarkable and heroic that such a beachhead has been taken and kept by groups like this one [*the Veritas Forum at Princeton University*]. It shows that even under the most adverse circumstances people recognize their need for God.

I don't think the future is as bleak as the past in terms of the intellectual world accepting the reality of the Creator. This has been the century for scientific materialism. The intellectual history of the 20th century has been a working out of what happened in the 19th century. What happened in the 19th century was that a new understanding of reality took hold – first in the intellectual world and then it gradually "trickled down" to the general populace.

Scientific materialism states that we are the products of purposeless material mechanisms. If materialism is true, then matter is all there is. To be realistic, we must account for its pervasive influence. Intellectual historians who speak of the leading figures of the 20th century usually name three: Darwin, Marx, and Freud. If there is a fourth, it will be Nietzsche, a philosopher, who proclaimed the death of God.

Now that we have moved beyond the 20th century, Freud and Marx have lost their scientific standing. Darwin is still around, but it is being scrutinized more since the atheistic materialistic system of the former Soviet Union collapsed. These systems just don't last forever. They eventually dissolve because of their own confusions. In the universities and in the intellectual life of the West, we see this scientific materialist understanding fracturing amid the confusion of relativism, intellectual nihilism, and deconstructionism.

Atheistic materialists hold the upper hand now and they broadly define a religious fanatic as anyone who believes in God.

Atheistic materialists hold the upper hand now and they broadly define a religious fanatic as anyone who believes in God. Atheistic materialists worry because they see the flaws and cracks developing in their own systems. It would be a big mistake, then, to get discouraged because the culture is stacked against us now. We will be marginalized, but there is opportunity to build the new intellectual world of the 21st century. It's an exciting time with exciting prospects.

Q7: What is your opinion about those who believe in God and evolution? Darwin believed in God. How do people who believe in evolution also believe in God?

Darwin didn't believe in God. Charles Darwin started out life as a nominal Christian, but was never very involved. During his life, he moved from his nominal Christianity to a firm agnosticism and then to a firm rejection of Christianity and theism of any kind. These changes came not only because of his theory, but also because he lost a daughter and felt this should not have happened if God existed. He was also influenced by his father, who was an outspoken unbeliever.

Darwin made this clear in his autobiography published posthumously. He never made it clear during his life partly because he did not want to prejudice people against his theory and partly because his wife was a very devout Christian. She obtained the manuscript of his autobiography and cut out of it all the parts which expressed his rejection of Christian theism. They were added back later so they are in editions you get today, but they were edited out of the original published version.

There have always been many Darwinists who felt they should try to tie the system to theism. They talk of guided evolution or theistic evolution. For example, Darwin's leading supporter in America in the early years was a Harvard botany professor named Asa Grey, who was a confirmed Christian. He said the system is perfectly compatible with Christianity, but he believed God provided the variations on which natural selection acted. For the first 70 or 80 years of evolution, there were many people who thought that way. My friend and staunch atheist, Professor William Provine of Cornell University, states that by 1900, most Darwinists were theists who saw evolution as some kind of divinely ordained and guided process.

That really changed in the 1920's and 1930's when the new version of Darwinism we call the *neo-Darwinian* synthesis came along. Whenever the subject of origins comes up today, Darwinists today—like Steven Jay Gould, William Provine, and Richard Dawkins—are absolutely emphatic that evolution as modern science understands it is a purposeless, unguided, completely mechanistic, completely materialistic system in which God plays no part. It is not ordained to produce human beings. Human beings are just an accidental by-product of it. This version of evolution, which is orthodox today, is very hard to reconcile with any meaningful theism. If a God is responsible for it, it is the most hands-off management you can imagine. The system is understood as something that runs on its own. Yet, many Christians today manage to convince themselves that the Darwinian system is true while they hold to very conservative theology.

The university culture goes like this – "you have your God and I have mine" and whatever works for you is OK by me as long as we don't believe God has any objective reality.

But where Darwinian doctrine has its greatest impact is in public. If you go to a university campus and make some reference to God, those hearing you are likely to think you are referring to God as something that exists in people's imagination. This results from Darwinism. The university culture goes like this – "you have your God and I have mine" and whatever works for you is OK by me as long as we don't believe God has any objective reality.

A theistic understanding of reality is seen as unimportant or irrelevant in academic departments. The modern university's understanding of God is that it is best studied as a subjective topic in anthropology and religion departments.

Q8: What do you think of different theories regarding the origin of species? What exactly do we know about creation scientifically?

I began to study Darwinian evolution because most people in the academic community in which I work "assume" science discovered a creation mechanism that is fundamentally different from the Christian account. I wanted to determine if anything in the scientific evidence, if fairly evaluated, denies the existence of a Creator. My investigation led me to believe there is really no basis for accepting the materialist account of creation.

You ask what we know about creation and that is difficult to assess. What we know now results from a research process that has gone on since the triumph of Darwinism more than a century ago. All the research we have currently is aimed at shoring up the Darwinian story and I suspect many things may need to be reconsidered.

The most likely understanding that best fits the evidence is that new kinds of things appeared during the course of the history of the earth over widely separated times – seemingly out of nowhere. Although there is no process of step-by-step materialistic development from preceding things, they are more or less like the preceding things. In other words, they are made of the same chemical materials and often like them in structure, but there is simply no understanding of how they got there.

New types of creatures consistently appear dated in the rocks in different ages fully formed just as they are and then they remain unchanged thereafter. Therefore, it seems there is a process of creation with unexplained appearances at varying times in the earth's history, absent some fundamental reconsideration of the geological record. That would be the best one can say.

I want to free people from the idea that somehow science has established an alternative to belief in God as Creator.

It is not true that the complexity of those creatures was built up by unintelligent material mechanisms. I want to use the scientific evidence to evaluate the scientific situation – not use it to argue people into a particular creation position so they will accept God. I only want to make others aware that nothing in the scientific evidence, when fairly considered, should shake their confidence that God is the Creator. I want to free people from the idea that somehow science has established an alternative to belief in God as Creator.

Q9: When a secular university audience hears you, many hear caricatures of the creation account, rather than your arguments. How do you address the popular Christian view of science which causes many academics to avoid the real issue?

It is definitely true that scientific materialists like to say, "Look at the alternative to evolution. It is Bible-thumpers." Their strategy is to ridicule Genesis and Noah's ark so they can avoid talking about the evidence for their own view. That is how the stereotype is used.

I urge creationists to stick to the fundamentals, but some think everything is fundamental. We should focus on the main point, which is creation by God.

That is why I never use Genesis in discussing this. Instead, I ask if there is evidence for the materialistic account of Darwinism. My opponents always bring up Genesis and ask, "How did they get all those animals on Noah's Ark?" This avoids the need to discuss the lack of evidence for the mutation selection mechanism as a way of creating genetic information.

I urge creationists to stick to the fundamentals, but some think everything is fundamental. We should focus on the main point, which is creation by God.

---

[1] Johnson, Phillip. *The Wedge of Truth* (Downers Grove, IL: InterVarsity Press, 2001).

[2] My personal story is on the *Christianity Today* and *ARN* websites and there is also a link to the ARN website (accessresearchnetwork.org) from the Christian Leadership Ministries' website (www.leaderu.com). Look for the "The Making of a Revolution" by Tim Stafford.

[3] This audience discussion was edited from transcriptions of Q&A sessions from two different lectures. The first four questions (Q1 thru Q4) were taken from a lecture Professor Johnson delivered at the *God and the Academy Conference* – a conference from which most essays in this volume were transcribed. The next six questions (Q5 thru Q9) were taken from a lecture Professor Johnson delivered at Princeton University during a *Veritas Forum* several years ago.

[4] Crick, Francis. *The Astonishing Hypothesis: The Scientific Search for the Soul* (New York: Scribner Publishing, 1994).

Chapter Four

—~∿∿∿~—

SHOULD METHODOLOGICAL NATURALISM CONSTRAIN SCIENCE?[1]

Alvin Plantinga

Dr. Alvin Plantinga has been called "the most important philosopher of religion now writing." Currently, he is the John A. O'Brien Professor of Philosophy and Director of the Center for Philosophy of Religion at the University of Notre Dame. He earned a M.A. from the University of Michigan and a Ph.D. from Yale University.

He has been president of the Western Division of the American Philosophical Association and president and co-founder of the Society of Christian Philosophers. Widely acclaimed for his work on the metaphysics of modality, the ontological argument, the problem of evil, and the epistemology of religious belief, he has authored or edited seven books, including, God and Other Minds, The Nature of Necessity, Warrant: the Current Debate, Warrant and Proper Function, and Warranted Christian Belief. Some of his articles in journals such as Theoria, American Philosophical Quarterly, Philosophical Studies, and the Journal of Philosophy, have been hailed as "masterpieces of the metaphysician's craft."

Abstract

According to Augustine, Kuyper, and many others, human history is dominated by a battle, a contest between the City of God (Civitas Dei) and the City of Man. Part of the task of the Christian community is to discern the limits and lineaments of this contest, to see how it plays out in intellectual life generally, and to pursue the various areas of intellectual life as citizens of the Civitas Dei. This naturally suggests pursuing science using all that we know – what we know about God, what we know about his creation, and what we know by faith -- as well as what we know in other ways. That natural suggestion is proscribed by the principle of methodological naturalism and, although it is widely accepted – and even exalted -- little can be said for it. When it is examined objectively, the arguments for it seem weak. Therefore, we should reject it, taken in its full generality. We can join others in Duhemian science and we should also pursue Augustinian science.

U NMATCHED FOR SWEEP AND ELOQUENCE, St. Augustine's *De Civitas Dei* is a magnificently powerful expression of a view of human history adopted by a host of later Christian thinkers.[2] According to that view, human history involves a struggle, a contest, a battle between what he calls the *Civitas Dei*, the City of God, on the one hand, and, on the other, the City of the World or the City of Man. The former is devoted to the worship and service of the Lord; the latter serves quite a different master.

Augustine believes that all of human history is to be understood in terms of this struggle, and nearly any cultural endeavor is involved in it. Modern natural science is an enormously important aspect of contemporary intellectual life. There are those cynics who see in science no more than technology — no more than a means of serving such practical ends as fighting disease and building bridges or space vehicles.

Surely, they are wrong. Science has done these important things, and so much more. It has given us powerful insights into ourselves and into the world God created. Science transformed our intellectual landscape and it is difficult to imagine what our intellectual life would be without it. If we follow Augustine, we should therefore expect that science, too, plays an important role in the contest he describes.

It would be naive to think contemporary science is religiously and theologically neutral .... Perhaps parts of science are like that .... But, many other areas of science are obviously and deeply involved in this clash between opposing worldviews.

According to an idea widely popular since the Enlightenment, however, science (at least when properly pursued) is a cool, reasoned, wholly dispassionate [3] attempt to find the truth about ourselves and our world, entirely independent of ideology, or moral convictions, or religious or theological commitments. Of course, this picture has lately developed some cracks. Sixteen centuries ago, Augustine saw that this common conception couldn't really be correct. It would be naive to think that contemporary science is religiously and theologically neutral—standing serenely above that Augustinian struggle and wholly irrelevant to it. Perhaps *parts* of science are like that: the size and shape of the earth and its distance from the sun, the periodic table of elements, the proof of the Pythagorean Theorem - these are all in a sense religiously neutral. But, many other areas of science are obviously and deeply involved in this clash between opposing worldviews. There is no neat recipe for telling which parts of science are neutral with respect to this contest and which are not, and of course what we have here is a continuum rather than a simple distinction. But here is a rough rule of thumb: the relevance of a bit of science to this contest depends upon how closely that bit is involved in the attempt to come to understand ourselves as human beings. Perhaps there is also another variable—how theoretical the bit in question is, in the sense of being directed at *understanding* as opposed to control.

It would be great to explore this area further—first, to try to say precisely what I mean in saying that science is not religiously neutral, and, second, to see exactly how Christianity bears on the understanding and practice of science. The first idea is not the focus of this paper and the second question requires vastly more knowledge of science than I can muster. That is a question not just for philosophers, but also for the Christian community of scientists and philosophers working together. What I shall do instead is vastly more programmatic.

I shall argue that a Christian academic and scientific community ought to pursue science in its own way, *starting from* and taking for granted what we know as Christians. (This suggestion suffers from the considerable disadvantage of being at present both unpopular and heretical. I shall argue, however, that it also has the considerable advantage of being correct.) Now one objection to this suggestion is enshrined in the dictum that science done properly necessarily involves methodological naturalism or (as Basil Willey calls it) provisional atheism.[4] This is the idea that science, properly so-called, cannot involve religious belief or commitment. My main aim in this paper is to explore, understand, discuss, and evaluate this claim and the arguments for it. I am painfully aware that what I have to say is tentative and incomplete, no more than a series of suggestions for research programs in Christian philosophy.

Weak Arguments for Methodological Naturalism

The natural thing to think is that the Christian scholarly community should do science in its own way and from its own perspective. What the Christian community really needs is a science that takes into account what we know as Christians. Indeed, this seems the rational thing in any event. After all, the rational thing is to use *all* that you know in trying to understand a given phenomenon. For example, when coming to a scientific understanding of hostility, or aggression, should Christian psychologists not make use of the notion of sin? In trying to achieve scientific understanding of love in its many and protean manifestations— or play, or music, or humor, or our sense of adventure, should we also not use what we know about humans as beings created in the image of God, who is himself the very source of love, beauty, and the like? And should we not do the same for morality? Consider that enormous, and impressive, and disastrous Bolshevik experiment of the twentieth century, perhaps the outstanding feature of the twentieth century political landscape: in coming to a scientific understanding of it, should Christians not use all that they know about human beings, including what they know by faith?

Hence, the sorts of hypotheses we investigate might involve such facts as human beings have been created by God in His image and have fallen into sin. These religious ideas might take a place in our science by way of various hypotheses.

True, there could be *practical* obstacles standing in the way of doing this; but in principle) the right way for the Christian community to attain scientific understanding of the way human beings are and behave, would be to start with what we know about human beings, including what we know about human nature by way of faith. Hence, the sorts of hypotheses we investigate might involve such facts as that human beings have been created by God in His image and have fallen into sin. These religious ideas might take a place in our science by way of explicitly entering various hypotheses. They might also play other roles: for example, they might be part of the background information with respect to which we evaluate the various scientific hypotheses and myths that come our way.

I say this is the natural thing to think. Oddly, the *denial* of this claim is widely taken for granted. As a matter of fact, it has achieved the status of philosophical orthodoxy. Among those who object to this claim are Christian thinkers with impressive credentials. Thus, Ernan McMullin:

> But, of course, methodological naturalism does not restrict our study of nature; it just lays down which sort of study qualifies as scientific. If someone wants to pursue another approach to nature - and there are many others— the methodological naturalist has no reason to object. Scientists have to proceed in this way; the methodology of natural science gives no purchase on the claim that a particular event or type of event is to be explained by invoking God's creative action directly. [5]

Part of the problem is to see more clearly what methodological naturalism is. Precisely what does it come to? Does it prohibit only the invoking of God's creative action *directly*, without the employment of secondary causes? Does it also proscribe invoking God's *indirect* creative action in explaining something scientifically? Does it pertain only to scientific *explanations*, but not to other scientific assertions and claims? Does it also preclude using claims about God's creative action, or other religious claims, as part of the background information with respect to which one tries to assess the probability of a proposed scientific explanation or account? We shall look into these matters later.

At the moment, however, I want to look into a different question: what reason is there for *accepting* the claim that science does indeed involve such a methodological naturalism, however exactly we construe the latter? I shall examine some proposed reasons for this claim and find them wanting. I shall then argue that nevertheless a couple of very sensible reasons lie behind at least part of this claim. These reasons, however, do not support the suggestion that science is religiously neutral.

Well then, what underlies the idea that science in some way necessarily involves this principle of methodological naturalism? First, and perhaps most important: this conception of science is an integral and venerable part of the whole conception of faith and reason we have inherited from the Enlightenment. I do not have the space to treat this topic with anything like the fullness it deserves; but the central idea, here, is that science is objective, public, sharable, publicly verifiable, and equally available to anyone, whatever their religious or metaphysical proclivities. We may be Buddhist, Hindu, Protestant, Catholic, Muslim, Jew, Baha'i, or none of the above: the findings of science hold equally for all of us. This is because proper science, as seen by the Enlightenment, is restricted to the deliverances of *reason* and *sense* (perception), which are the same for all people. Religion, on the other hand, is private, subjective, and obviously subject to considerable individual differences. But if science *is* indeed public and sharable by all, then of course one cannot properly pursue it by starting from some bit of religious belief or dogma.

One root of this way of thinking about science is a consequence of the modern foundationalism stemming from Descartes and perhaps even more importantly, Locke. Modern classical foundationalism has come in for a lot of criticism lately, and I do not propose to add my voice to the howling mob.[6] And since the classical foundationalism upon which methodological naturalism is based has run aground, I shall instead consider some more local, less grand, and cosmic reasons for accepting methodological naturalism.

Methodological Naturalism Is True by Definition

So *why* must a scientist proceed in accordance with methodological naturalism? Michael Ruse suggests that methodological naturalism, or part of it, is *true by definition*:

> Furthermore, even if Scientific Creationism were totally successful in making its case as science, it would not yield a scientific explanation of origins. Rather, at

most, it could prove that science shows that there can be no scientific explanation of origins. The Creationists believe that the world started miraculously. But miracles lie outside of science, which by definition deals only with the natural, the repeatable, that which is governed by law. [7]

Ruse's claim apparently rules out hypotheses that include references to God. God is a supernatural being and hypotheses referring to him therefore deal with something besides the natural. Hence, such hypotheses cannot be part of science.

Ruse suggests that methodological naturalism is true by definition of the term science one supposes. Ruse apparently holds that there is a correct definition of science, such that from the definition, it follows that science deals only with what is natural, repeatable, and governed by law. (Note that this claim does not bear on the suggestions that a Christian scientist can propose hypotheses involving such religious doctrines as original sin, and can evaluate the epistemic probability of a scientific hypothesis relative to background belief that includes Christian belief.) Ruse's claim apparently rules out hypotheses that include references to God. God is a supernatural being and hypotheses referring to him therefore deal with something besides the natural. Hence, such hypotheses cannot be part of science.

Three things are particularly puzzling about Ruse's claim. *First,* enormous energy has been expended, for at least several centuries, on the demarcation problem: the problem of giving necessary and sufficient conditions for distinguishing science from other human activities.[8] This effort has apparently failed; but if in fact there *were* a definition of the sort Ruse is appealing to, then presumably there would be available a set of necessary and sufficient conditions for something to be considered science. Ruse does not address the many and (I think) successful arguments for the conclusion that there is no such set of necessary and sufficient conditions, let alone such a definition of the term science; he simply declares that—by definition—science has the properties he mentions.

Second, Ruse here proposes three properties that he says are by definition characteristic of any bit of science: that it deals with things that (a) are repeatable, (b) are merely natural, and (c) are governed by natural law. But take repeatability, and consider this passage by Andrei Linde: speaking of the Big Bang, he says, "One might think it very difficult to extract useful and reliable information from the unique experiment carried out about 10^9 years ago."[9] According to Linde, the Big Bang is unique and therefore, presumably, unrepeatable—at any rate it *might* turn out to be unrepeatable. If so, would we be obliged to conclude that contemporary cosmological inquiries into the nature of the Big Bang and into the early development of the universe are not really part of science?

Consider next the property of being governed by law. The very existence of natural law is controversial; Bas van Fraassen, for example, has given an extended and formidable argument for the conclusion that there are no natural laws.[10] There are *regularities*, but a regularity is not yet a law; a law is what is supposed to *explain and ground* a regularity. Furthermore, a law is supposed to hold with some kind of *necessity*, typically thought to be less stringent than broadly logical necessity, but necessity nonetheless.[11] This idea of lawfulness is an inheritance of Enlightenment deism, and here, as elsewhere, Enlightenment deism misses the mark.

Perhaps the demand for law cannot be met. Perhaps there are regularities, but no laws; perhaps there is nothing like the necessity allegedly attaching to laws. Perhaps the best way to think of these alleged laws is as universally, or nearly universally quantified, counterfactuals of divine freedom.[12] Suppose van Fraassen is right and there are no natural laws, would it follow by definition that there is not any science? That seems too strong. For all we know, there are some laws, but they do not govern everything. This is how it is with earthquakes, the weather, and radioactive decay. Would it follow that one could not study these things scientifically?

The *third* puzzling thing about Ruse's claim: it is hard to see how anything like a reasonably serious dispute about what is and is not science could be settled just by appealing to a definition. One thinks this would work only if the original query were really a verbal question—a question like, *"Is the English word science properly applicable to a hypothesis that makes reference to God?"* But that was not the question: the question is instead, *"Could a hypothesis that makes reference to God be part of science?"* That question cannot be answered just by citing a definition.

Does Functional Integrity Require Methodological Naturalism?

Diogenes Allen, John Stek, and Howard Van Till answer that functional integrity requires methodological naturalism. According to Van Till, God has created a world characterized by functional integrity:

> By this term I mean to denote a created world that has no functional deficiencies, no gaps in its economy of the sort that would require God to act immediately, temporarily assuming the role of creature to perform functions within the economy of the created world that other creatures have not been equipped to perform.[13]

Van Till seems to be directing his fire at only one of the several ways in which Christians might employ what they know by faith in pursuing natural science; he is arguing that a scientific hypothesis cannot properly claim that God does something *immediately* or *directly*. (Note also that the claim here is not that such a hypothesis would not be *scientific*, but that it would be false.) What he says seems to be consistent, so far as I can tell, with the claim (say) that in doing their psychology Christian psychologists can properly appeal to the fact that human beings have been created in the image of God, or are subject to original sin.

Suppose we turn to Van Till's proscription of hypotheses to the effect that God has done something or other immediately or directly. This idea of direct action conceals pitfalls and deserves more by way of concentrated attention than I can give it here.[14] The basic idea, however, is fairly clear. An example of *indirect* divine creation would be my building a house; we may say that *God* creates the house, but does so indirectly, by employing *my* activity as a means. God acts indirectly if he brings about some effect by employing as a means the activity of something else he has created. God acts directly, then, if and only if he brings about some effect, and does not do so by way of employing as a means the activity of some created being.

Van Till suggests that God does nothing at all in the world *directly*; only *creatures* do things directly. But, Van Till, like any other theist, would agree that God directly conserves the world and all its creatures in being; he is directly active not only in the Big Bang, but also in the sparrow's fall. Were he to suspend this constant conserving activity, the world would disappear like a dream upon awakening. And no doubt Van Till would also agree (on pain of infinite regress) that if God does anything in the world indirectly, he also does something directly: presumably he cannot cause an effect indirectly without also, at some point, acting directly, creating something directly. Van Till must therefore be understood in some other way. Perhaps his idea is that God created the universe at some time in the *past* (acting directly at that time), but since then, he never acts directly in the world, except for conserving his creation in being, and miracles connected with salvation history. But why think a thing like that? Consider the fact that Christians as diverse as Pope Pius XII and John Calvin have thought that God created human souls directly; can we simply assume without argument that they are mistaken? What is the warrant for supposing that God no longer acts directly in the world?

[Van Till argues] that a scientific hypothesis cannot properly claim that God does something immediately or directly.

Van Till appeals for support, for this theological position, to Allen and Stek. Allen asserts that,

> God can never properly be used in scientific accounts, which are formulated in terms of the relations between the members of the universe, because that would reduce God to the status of a creature. According to a Christian conception of God as creator of a universe that is rational through and through, there are no missing relations between the members of nature. If in our study of nature, we run into what seems to be an instance of a connection missing between members of

nature, the Christian doctrine of creation implies that
we should keep looking for one.[15]

Allen's suggestion seems to imply, not just that Christians cannot
properly propose, as part of science, that God has done something
directly, but also that it would be out of order to appeal, in science, to
such ideas as that human beings have been created in God's image. This
idea is not a matter of saying how things in the world are related to each
other; it is instead a matter of saying how some things in the world —
we human beings—are related to God. Allen believes that scientific
accounts must always be formulated in terms of the relationships
between members of the universe (and if that is true, then perhaps, as
he says, referring to God in science would be to reduce him to a
creature). Taken at face value, however, this seems hasty. A textbook on
astronomy may tell you what the diameter of Jupiter is (or how old the
earth, or the sun, or the Milky Way is). This does not tell you how
things in the world stand related to each other, but instead just tells you
something about one of those things; it is science nonetheless.

---

*Allen's main point is that a scientific account cannot properly be
formulated in terms of the relationship of anything to God. But,
why not?*

Allen's main point is that a scientific account cannot properly be
formulated in terms of the relationship of anything to God. But why
not? What is the authority for this claim? Does not it seem arbitrary?
Consider the truth that human beings have been created in the image of
God, but have also fallen into sin. This dual truth might turn out to be
very useful in giving psychological explanations of various phenomena.
If it is, why should a Christian psychologist not employ it? Why would
the result not be science? It could be that investigation would suggest
that God created life directly, that it did not arise through the agency of
other created things. If that is how things turn out, or how things appear
at a given time, why not say so? And why not say so as part of science?

As a Christian, you believe that God made the world and could have done so in many different ways; why not employ this knowledge in evaluating the probability of various hypotheses (for example, the Grand Evolutionary Myth)? Christians also have beliefs about what is rational in Simon's sense, i.e., about what sorts of goals a properly functioning human being will have. Christians also have beliefs about what sorts of actions are in their own or someone else's best interests. Why not employ these beliefs in making a scientific evaluation of the probability of, say, Simon's account of altruism, or in giving her own account of these phenomena?

Finally, consider John Stek:

> Since the created realm is replete with its own economy that is neither incomplete (God is not a component within it) nor defective, understanding based on both practical experience and scientific endeavors—*we must methodologically exclude all notions of immediate divine causality*. As stewards of the creation, we must methodologically honor the principle that creation interprets creation; indeed, we must honor that principle as religiously as the theologian must honor the principle that "Scripture interprets Scripture"—or, since Scripture presupposes general revelation, that revelation interprets revelation. In pursuit of a stewardly understanding of the creation, we may not introduce a "God of the gaps," not even in the as-yet mysterious realm of subatomic particles. We may not do so (1) because God is not an internal component within the economy of the created realm, and (2) because to do so would be to presume to exercise power over God—the presumptuous folly of those in many cultures who have claimed to be specialists in the manipulation of divine powers (e.g., shamans in Russian folk religion and medicine men in primitive cultures).[16]

Stek insists that we must methodologically exclude all notions of immediate divine causality in our understanding of the created realm.

One of his reasons seems to be that to appeal to a notion of immediate divine causality would introduce a God of the gaps, and to do *that* would presume to exercise power over God. But, am I really presuming to exercise power over God, for example, by concurring with John Calvin and Pope Pius XII, and many others, that God directly creates human souls? Or in claiming that he created life specially? At best, this requires more argument.

Stek insists that "we must methodologically exclude all notions of immediate divine causality" in our understanding of the created realm.

As Stek says, God isn't an internal component within the created realm. It hardly follows, however, that he does not act immediately or directly in the created realm; like any theist, Stek too would agree that God directly and immediately conserves his creation in existence. And would not he also agree that if God creates anything indirectly, then he creates some things directly? So I am not sure why Stek thinks that we must observe this methodological naturalism. Why think that God does not do anything directly or create anything directly? What is the reason for thinking this? Scripture does not suggest it; there do not seem to be arguments from any other source; why then accept it?

These reasons, then, for the necessity or advisability of methodological naturalism do not seem strong; and since they *are* so weak, it is reasonable to surmise they do not really represent what is going on in the minds of those who offer them. I suggest there is a different and unspoken reason for this obeisance to methodological naturalism: *fear and loathing of God-of-the-gaps theology.* As we saw above, Stek declares that, "In pursuit of a stewardly understanding of the creation, we may not introduce a 'God of the gaps'"; he, together with the other three authors I have cited in this connection (McMullin, Van Till and Allen), explicitly mention God-of-the-gaps theology and explicitly connect it with methodological naturalism via the suggestion that God has done this or that immediately. To hold that God acts directly in creation is to fall into, or anyway lean dangerously close to this sort of theology. But is this true? Precisely, what is God-of-the-gaps theology?

There is not anything that it is *precisely*; it is not that sort of thing. Somewhat vaguely, however, it can be characterized as follows. The God-of-the-gaps theologian is an Enlightenment semi-deist who thinks of the universe as a vast machine working according to a set of necessary and inviolable natural laws. (Perhaps a God has created the universe: but if he did, it is now for the most part self-sufficient and self-contained.) These natural laws, furthermore, have a kind of majesty; they are necessary in some strong sense; perhaps not even God, if there is such a person, could violate them; but even if he could, he almost certainly would not. (Hence the otherwise inexplicable worry about miracles characteristic of this sort of thought.) Natural science investigates and lays out the structure of this cosmic machine, in particular by trying to discover and lay bare those laws, and to explain the phenomena in terms of them. There seem to be *some* phenomena, however, that resist a naturalistic explanation – so far, at any rate. We should therefore postulate a deity in terms of whose actions we can explain these things that current science cannot. Newton's suggestion that God periodically adjusts the orbits of the planets is often cited as just such an example of God-of-the-gaps theology.

The following, therefore, are the essential points of God-of-the-gaps theology. First, the world is a vast machine that is almost entirely self-sufficient; divine activity in nature is limited to those phenomena for which there is no scientific, i.e., mechanical and naturalistic explanation. Second, the existence of God is a kind of large-scale hypothesis postulated to explain what cannot be explained otherwise, i.e., naturalistically.[17] Third, there is the apologetic emphasis: the best or one of the best reasons for believing that there is such a person as God is the fact that there are phenomena that natural science cannot (so far) explain naturalistically.

Now McMullin, Stek, Van Till, and Allen all object strenuously to God-of-the-gaps theology - and rightly so. This line of thought is at best a kind of anemic and watered-down semi-deism that inserts God's activity into the gaps in scientific knowledge; it is associated, furthermore, with a weak and pallid apologetic according to which perhaps the main source or motivation for belief in God is that there are some things science cannot presently explain. A far cry indeed from what the Scriptures teach! God-of-the-gaps theology is worlds apart from serious Christian theism. This is evident at the following points.

First, and most important, according to serious theism, God is constantly, immediately, intimately, and directly active in his creation. He constantly upholds it in existence and providentially governs it. He is immediately and directly active in everything from the Big Bang to the sparrow's fall. Literally nothing happens without his upholding hand.[18]

Second, natural laws are not in any way independent of God, and are perhaps best thought of as regularities in the ways in which he treats the stuff he has made, or perhaps as counterfactuals of divine freedom. (Hence there is nothing untoward in the thought that on some occasions, God might do something in a way different from his usual way- e.g., raise someone from the dead or change water into wine.) Indeed, the whole *interventionist* terminology - speaking of God as *intervening* in nature, or *intruding* into it, or *interfering* with it, or *violating* natural law – all this goes with God-of-the-gaps theology, not with serious theism. According to the latter, God is already and always intimately acting in nature, which depends from moment to moment for its existence upon immediate divine activity; there is not and could not be any such thing as his intervening in nature.

These are broadly speaking metaphysical differences between Christian theism and God-of-the-gaps thought. Furthermore, there are equally significant epistemological differences. First, the thought that there is such a person as God is not, according to Christian theism, a hypothesis postulated to *explain* something or other,[19] nor is the main reason for believing that there is such a person as God the fact that there are phenomena that elude the best efforts of current science.[20] Rather, our knowledge of God comes by way of *general* revelation, which involves something like Aquinas' general knowledge of God or Calvin's *sensus divinitatis*, and also, and more importantly, by way of God's *special* revelation, in the Scriptures and through the church, of his plan for dealing with our fall into sin.

God-of-the-gaps theology, therefore, is every bit as bad as McMullin, Van Till, Stek, and Allen think. (Indeed, it may be worse than Van Till and Stek think, since some of the things they think—in particular their ban on God's acting directly in nature—seems to me to display a decided list in the direction of such theology). Serious Christians should indeed resolutely reject this way of thinking. The Christian community knows that God is constantly active in his creation, that natural laws, if there are any, are not independent of God, and that the existence of God is certainly not a hypothesis designed to explain what science cannot. Furthermore, the Christian community begins the scientific enterprise already believing in God; it does not (or at any rate need not) engage in it for apologetic reasons, either with respect to itself or with respect to non-Christians.

But, from these things, it does not follow for an instant that the Christian scientific community should endorse methodological naturalism.

But, from these things, it does not follow for an instant that the Christian scientific community should endorse methodological naturalism. The Christian community faces these questions: How shall we best understand this creation God has made, and in which he has placed us? What is the best way to proceed? What information can we or shall we use? Is it not clear initially, at any rate, that we should employ whatever is useful and enlightening, including what we know about God and his relationship to the world, and including what we know by way of special revelation? Could we not sensibly conclude, for example, that God created life, or human life, or something else specially? (I do not say we *should* conclude that: I say only that we *could*, and should if that is what the evidence most strongly suggests.) Should we not use our knowledge of sin and creation in psychology, sociology, and the human sciences in general? Should we not evaluate various scientific theories by way of a background body of belief that includes what we know about God and what we know specifically as Christians? Should we not decide what needs explanation against that same background body of beliefs?

If not, why not? That certainly seems initially to be the rational thing to do (one should make use of all that one knows in trying to come to an understanding of some phenomenon) and it is hard to see anything like strong reasons against it. We certainly do not fall into any of unhappy ways of thinking characteristic of God-of-the-gaps theology just by doing one of these things. In doing them, we do not thereby commit ourselves, for example, to the idea that God does almost nothing directly in nature, or that the universe is something like a vast machine in whose workings God could intervene only with some difficulty; nor are we thereby committed to the idea that one of our main reasons for belief in God is just that there are things science cannot explain, or that the idea of God is really something like a large-scale hypothesis postulated to explain those things. Not at all. The whole God-of-the-gaps issue is nothing but a red herring in the present context.[21]

Two Stronger Arguments for Methodological Naturalism

These arguments, therefore, are not convincing; but there are two stronger arguments for embracing methodological naturalism in the practice of science. The first of these really deserves a paper all to itself, but here, I shall treat it briefly.

Duhemian Science

We can approach this argument by thinking about some striking passages in Pierre Duhem's *The Aim and Structure of Physical Theory.*[22] Duhem was both a serious Catholic and a serious scientist; he was accused (as he thought) by Abel Rey of allowing his religious and metaphysical views as a Christian to enter his physics in an improper way.[23] Duhem repudiated this suggestion, claiming that his Christianity did not enter his physics in an improper way, because it did not enter his physics in any way at all.[24] Furthermore, he thought the *correct* or *proper* way to pursue physical theory was the way in which he had in fact done it; physical theory should be completely independent of religious or metaphysical views or commitments.

He thought this for two reasons. *First*, he thought religion bore little relevance to physical theory: "Was it not a glaring fact to us, as to any man of good sense, that the object and nature of physical theory are things foreign to religious doctrines and without any contact with them?"[25]

But there is something deeper. Although Duhem may have thought that *religious* doctrines had little to do with physical theory, he did not at all think the same thing about *metaphysical* doctrines. In fact, he believed that metaphysical doctrines had often entered deeply into physical theory. Many theoretical physicists, as he saw it, took it that the principal aim of physics is to *explain* observable phenomena. Explanation is a slippery notion and a complex phenomenon; but here at any rate the relevant variety of explanation involves giving an account of the phenomena, the appearances, in terms of the nature or constitution of the underlying material reality. He goes on to give a striking illustration, recounting how atomists, Aristotelians, Newtonians, and Cartesians differ in the explanations or accounts they give of the phenomena of magnetism: atomists give the requisite explanation, naturally enough, in terms of atoms; Cartesians in terms of pure extensions; and Aristotelians in terms of matter and form.[26] The differences among these explanations, he says, are metaphysical; they pertain to the ultimate nature or constitution of matter. But, if the aim is to explain the phenomena in terms of the ultimate nature or constitution of matter, then it is crucially important to get the latter right, to get the right answer to the metaphysical question "What is the nature or constitution of matter?" In this way, he says, physical theory is subordinated to metaphysics: Therefore, if the aim of physical theories is to explain experimental laws, theoretical physics is not an autonomous science; it is subordinate to metaphysics.[27]

Well, what is the matter with that? The problem, Duhem says, is that if you think of physics in this way, then your estimate of the worth of a physical theory will depend upon the metaphysics you adopt. Physical theory will be dependent upon metaphysics in such a way that someone who does not accept the metaphysics involved in a given physical theory cannot accept the physical theory either. And the problem with that is that the disagreements that run riot in metaphysics will ingress into physics, so that the latter cannot be an activity we can all work at together, regardless of our metaphysical views:

> Now to make physical theories depend on metaphysics
> is surely not the way to let them enjoy the privilege of
> universal consent. If theoretical physics is subordinated

to metaphysics, the divisions separating the diverse metaphysical systems will extend into the domain of physics. A physical theory reputed to be satisfactory by the sectarians of one metaphysical school will be rejected by the partisans of another school.[28]

So here we have another argument for methodological naturalism, and a simple, commonsense one at that: it is important that we all—Christian, naturalist, creative antirealist, whatever—be able to work at physics and the other sciences together and cooperatively; therefore we should not employ in science views, commitments, and assumptions only some of us accept. That is, we should not employ them in a way that would make the theory of science in question unacceptable or less acceptable to someone who did not share the commitment or assumption in question. [29] But, then we cannot employ, in that way, such ideas as that the world and things therein have been designed and created by God. Proper science, insofar as it is to be common to all of us, will have to eschew any dependence upon metaphysical and religious views held by only some of us; therefore we should endorse methodological naturalism. We do not, of course, have to be metaphysical naturalists in order to pursue *Duhemian* science; but if science is to be properly universal, it cannot employ assumptions or commitments that are not universally shared.

Duhemian science, therefore, is maximally inclusive; we can all do it together and agree on its results. But what about those who, like Simon, for example, think it is important also to do a sort of human science which starts, not from methodological naturalism, but from metaphysical naturalism? And what about those who, like the atomists, Cartesians, and Aristotelians think it is important to pursue a sort of science in which the aim is successful explanation in terms of underlying unobservable realities? And what about Christians or theists, who propose to investigate human reality employing all that they know, including what they know as Christians or theists? So far as Duhem's claims go, there is nothing improper about any of this. Should we call this kind of activity science; does it deserve that honorific term? There is no reason in Duhem for a negative answer. It is important, to see that science of this sort is not Duhemian science and does not have the claim to universal assent enjoyed by the latter; but of course that is nothing against it.

According to the fuller Duhemian picture, then, we would all work together on Duhemian science; but each of the groups involved—naturalists and theists, for example, but perhaps others as well—could then go on to incorporate Duhemian science into a fuller context that includes the metaphysical or religious principles specific to that group. Let us call this broader science Augustinian science. Of course, the motivation for doing this will vary enormously from area to area. Physics and chemistry are overwhelmingly Duhemian[30] (of course the same might not be true for *philosophy* of physics); here perhaps Augustinian science would be for the most part irrelevant pointless otiose. The same goes for biological sciences: surely much that goes on there could be thought of as Duhemian science. On the other hand, there are also non-Duhemian elements in the neighborhood, such as those declarations of certainty and the claims that evolutionary biology shows that human and other forms of life must be seen as a result of chance (and hence cannot be thought of as designed). In the human sciences, however, vast stretches are clearly non-Duhemian; it is in these areas that Augustinian science would be most relevant and important.

Should the Christian scientific community observe the constraints of methodological naturalism? The answer seems to be yes, in those areas where Duhemian science is possible and valuable. But, the Christian scientific community should also engage in non-Duhemian, Augustinian science where that is relevant. Nothing here suggests that, "if it ain't Duhemian, it ain't science."

So return to our central question: should the Christian scientific community observe the constraints of methodological naturalism? So far as this argument is concerned, the answer seems to be yes, in those areas where Duhemian science is possible and valuable. But, the Christian scientific community should also engage in non-Duhemian, Augustinian science where that is relevant. Nothing here suggests that, "if it ain't Duhemian, it ain't science."

Science Stoppers?

There is still another reason for methodological naturalism; this one, too, is commonsense simplicity itself. God has created this whole wonderful and awful (both taken in their etymological senses) world of ours. One of the things we want to do as his creatures is to understand the world he has made, see (to the extent that we can) how it is made, what its structure is, and how it works. This is not, of course, the only thing God's children must do with the world; we must also appreciate it, care for it, love it, thank the Lord for it, and see his hand in it. But understanding it is valuable, and so is understanding it in a theoretical way. One way of understanding something is to see how it is made, how it is put together, and how it works. That is what goes on in natural science. The object of this science is nature; for Christians, its aim (one of its aims) is to see what the structure of this world is and how it works; this is a way of appreciating God's creation, and part of what it is to exercise the image of God in which we have been created.

There will be little advance along this front if, in answer to the question, *"Why does so and so work the way it does?"* or *"What is the explanation of so and so?"* we often reply, *"Because God did it that way"* or *"Because it pleased God that it should be like that."* This will often be true,[31] but it is not the sort of answer we want at that juncture. It goes without saying that God has in one way or another brought it about that the universe displays the character it does; but what we want to know in science are the answers to questions like, *"What is this made out of? What is its structure? How does it work? How is it connected with other parts of God's creation?"* Claims to the effect that God has done this or that (created life, or created human life) directly are science stoppers. If this claim is true, then presumably we cannot go on to learn something further about how it was done or how the phenomenon in question works; if God did it directly, there will be nothing further to find out. *How does it happen that there is such a thing as light? Well, God said, "Let there be light" and there was light.* This is true and of enormous importance, but if taken as science, it is not helpful. It does not help us find out more about light, what its physical character is, how it is related to other things, and the like. Ascribing something to the direct action of God tends to cut off further inquiry.

This is a reason for only *part* of methodological naturalism. There are several *different* ways in which Christianity might enter into the texture of science: (1) stating and employing hypotheses according to which God does things directly; (2) stating and employing hypotheses according to which he does things indirectly; (3) evaluating theories with respect to background information that includes Christian theism; (4) employing such propositions as *human beings have been created in God's image*, either directly or as background; (5) doing the same for such doctrines as that of original sin, which do not involve any direct mention of God at all; and (6) deciding what needs explanation by way of referring to that same background. The considerations cited in the last paragraph are at best a reason for a proscription of (1).

The claim that God has directly created life, for example, may be a science stopper, but it does not follow that God did not directly create life.

But, they are not even much of a reason for that. The claim that God has directly created life, for example, may be a science stopper; it does not follow that God *did not* directly create life. Obviously we have no guarantee that God has done everything by way of employing secondary causes, or in such a way as to encourage further scientific inquiry, or for our convenience as scientists, or for the benefit of the National Science Foundation. Clearly we cannot sensibly insist in advance that whatever we are confronted with is to be explained in terms of something *else* God did; he must have done *some* things directly. It would be worth knowing, if possible, which things he *did* do directly; to know this would be an important part of a serious and profound knowledge of the universe. The fact that such claims are science stoppers means that as a general rule they will not be helpful; it does not mean that they are never true, and it does not mean that they can never be part of a proper scientific theory. Of course, it does not even bear on the other ways in which Christianity or Christian theism can be relevant to science, viz. (2) through (6) above. It is a giant and unwarranted step from the recognition that claims of direct divine activity are "science stoppers" to the insistence that science must pretend the created universe is just there, refusing to recognize that it is indeed *created*.

It is a giant and unwarranted step from the recognition that claims of direct divine activity are "science stoppers" to the insistence that science must pretend the created universe is just there, refusing to recognize that it is indeed created.

There is little to be said for methodological naturalism. At its best, it tells us only that Duhemian science must be metaphysically neutral and that claims of direct divine action will not ordinarily make for good science. Even in these two cases, what we have reason for is not a principled proscription, but a general counsel, that in some circumstances is quite clearly inapplicable. There is no reason to proscribe a question like, *"Did God create life specially?"* There is no reason why such a question cannot be investigated empirically[32] and there is no reason to proscribe in advance an affirmative answer.

Christian thought (particularly since the High Middle Ages) as opposed to Greek (and in particular Aristotelian)[33] thought contains a strong tendency to see the world as through and through *contingent*. The world need not have existed; that is, God need not have created it. The world need not have had just the structure it does have; that is, God could have created it differently. This sense of the contingency of nature has been one important source of the emphasis upon the *empirical* character of modern science. As a rough rule of thumb, we can say that it is by *reason*, by *a priori* thought, that we learn of what cannot be otherwise; it is by the senses, by way of a *posteriori* inquiry that we learn about what is contingent.[34] But the world as God created it is full of contingencies. Therefore, we do not merely think about it in our armchairs, trying to infer from first principles how many teeth there are in a horse's mouth; instead we take a look. The same apply to the question of how God acts in the world: here we should rely less upon *a priori* theology and more upon empirical inquiry. We have no good grounds for insisting that God *must* do things one specific way; so far as we can see, he is free to do things in many different ways. So perhaps he did create human life specially; or perhaps he has done other things specially. We cannot properly rule this out in advance by way of appeal to speculative theology; we should look and see.

Conclusion

My main point can be summarized as follows. According to Augustine, Kuyper, and many others, human history is dominated by a battle—a contest between the *Civitas Dei* and the City of Man. Part of the task for the Christian academic is to discern the limits of this contest and to pursue the various areas of intellectual life as citizens of the *Civitas Dei*. This naturally suggests pursuing science using all that we know—what we know about God and his creation and what we know by faith—and what we know in other ways.

Although widely accepted—and even exalted —little can be said for methodological naturalism. When examined objectively, the arguments for it seem weak. Therefore, we should reject it in its entirety and join others in Duhemian science while also pursuing our own Augustinian science.

That natural suggestion is proscribed by the principle of methodological naturalism. Although widely accepted—and even exalted—little can be said for methodological naturalism. When examined objectively, the arguments for it seem weak. Therefore, we should reject it in its entirety and join others in Duhemian science while also pursuing our own Augustinian science.

In conclusion, I refer to another statement by John Stek. He said,

> Theology must take account of all that humanity comes to know about the world and science must equally take account of all that we come to know about God. In fact, we cannot, without denying our being and vocation as stewards, pursue theology without bringing to that study all that we know about the

world, nor can we, without denying our being and vocation as stewards, pursue science without bringing to that study all that we know about God.[35]

Just so.

---

[1] This essay is reprinted from Perspectives on Science and Christian Faith 49 (September 1997): 143-154.

[2] For example, many Reformed Christians follow Abraham Kuyper in holding that intellectual endeavor in general and natural science in particular are not independent of religious commitment. Perhaps the credit for this idea should go not to Augustine, but to Tertullian. Tertullian has suffered from a bad press; one of his major emphases, however, is that scholarship- intellectual endeavor- is not religiously neutral.

[3] The idea is not, of course, that a scientist will not be passionate either about science generally, or his favorite theories, or his reputation; it is rather that none of these properly enters into the evaluation of a scientific theory or explanation.

[4] Science must be provisionally atheistic or cease to be itself. B. Willey, "Darwin's Place in the History of Thought," in Darwinism and the Study of Society, edited by M. Banton (Chicago: Quadrangle Books, 1961): 1-16. Willey does not mean, of course, that one who proceeds in this way is properly accused of atheism. In the same way, to call this procedure or proscription methodological naturalism is not to imply that one who proceeds in this way is really a naturalist. See E. McMullin, "Plantinga's Defense of Special Creation," Christian Scholar's Review 21 (September, 1991): 57.

[5] McMullin, E. "Plantinga's Defense," 57.

[6] I have argued elsewhere that one condition of rationality laid down by modern classical foundationalism is in fact self-referentially incoherent. See, for example, "Reason and Belief in God," in Faith and Rationality, edited by A. Plantinga and N. Wolterstorff (Notre Dame: University of Notre Dame Press, 1983): 60ff.

[7] Ruse, Michael. Darwinism Defended (Reading: Addison-Wesley, 1982): 322 (my italics).

[8] See, for example, L. Laudan, "The Demise of the Demarcation Problem," in But Is It Science? ed. M. Ruse (New York: Prometheus Books, 1988): 337-50.

[9] Linde, A. D. "Particle Physics and Inflationary Cosmology," Physics Today (September, 1987): 61.

[10] See B. van Fraassen, Laws and Symmetry (Oxford: Oxford University Press, 1989): chapters. 2-5.

[11] See, for example, D. Armstrong, What Is a Law of Nature? (Cambridge: Cambridge University Press, 1983): 39ff.

[12] That is, propositions that state how God (freely) treats the things he has made, and how he would have treated them had things been relevantly different. Nearly universally quantified: if we think of them this way, we can think of miracles as going

contrary to law without thinking of them (inconsistently) as exceptions to some universal and necessary proposition.

[13] Van Till, H. J. "When Faith and Reason Cooperate," *Christian Scholar's Review* 21 (September, 1991): 42.

[14] See, for example, W. P. Alston, "Divine and Human Action," in *Divine and Human Action: Essays in the Metaphysics of Theism*, edited by T. Morris (Ithaca: Cornell University Press, 1988): 257-80.

[15] Allen, D. *Christian Belief in a Postmodern* World (Louisville: Westminster/John Knox Press, 1989): 45.

[16] Stek, J. H. "What Says the Scriptures?" in *Portraits of Creation: Biblical and Scientific Perspectives on the World's Formation*, edited by H. J. Van Till, R. E. Snow, J. H. Stek, and D. A. Young (Grand Rapids: William B. Eerdmans Publishing Company, 1990): 261.

[17] I do not mean to suggest that one who espouses or advocates God-of-the-gaps theology himself or herself believes in God only as such a hypothesis: that is quite another question.

[18] In addition, most medieval Christian thinkers have also insisted on a separate divine activity of God's; any causal transaction in the world requires his *concurrence*. Problems arise here; to some ears it sounds as if this doctrine is motivated less by the relevant evidence than by a desire to pay metaphysical compliments to God.

[19] See my "Is Theism Really a Miracle?" *Faith and Philosophy* 3 no. 2 (1986): 132ff.

[20] A further problem with this way of thinking: as science explains more and more, the scope for God's activity is less and less; it is in danger of being squeezed out of the world altogether, thus making more and more tenuous one's reasons (on this way of thinking) for believing that there is such a person as God at all. (Of course, it must also be acknowledged on the other side that things sometimes go in the opposite direction; for example, it is much harder now than it was in Darwin's day to see how it could be that life should arise just by way of the regularities recognized in physics and chemistry.)

[21] Further, Newton seems to me to have suffered a bum rap. He suggested that God made periodic adjustments in the orbits of the planets: true enough. But he did not propose this as a reason for believing in God; it is rather that (of course) he already believed in God, and could not think of any other explanation for the movements of the planets. He turned out to be wrong; he could have been right, however, and in any event he was not endorsing any of the characteristic ideas of God-of-the-gaps thought.

[22] Duhem, P. (1906) *The Aim and Structure of Physical Theory*, translated by P. P. Wiener, with the foreword by Prince Louis de Broglie (Princeton: Princeton University Press, 1954).

[23] Rey, A. "La Philosophie Scientifique de M. Duhem," *Révue de Metaphysique et de Morale* 12 (July, 1904): 699ff.

[24] See the appendix to *The Aim and Structure of Physical Theory*, which is entitled "Physics of a Believer" and is a reprint of Duhem's reply to Rey; it was originally published in the *Annales de Philosophie Chrtienne* 1 (October and November, 1905): 44f. and 133f.

[25] Duhem, 278.

[26] Ibid., 10-18.

[27] Ibid., 10.

[28] Ibid., 10.

[29] This would not preclude, of course, employing such ideas in theories proposed, not as true, but only as empirically adequate.

[30] The Principle of Indifference is non-Duhemian, but it is not easy to find other examples. (I am assuming that *interpretations* of quantum mechanics [as opposed to quantum mechanics itself] belong to philosophy rather than physics.).

[31] Though not always: if the question is *Why was there such a thing as WW II?*, the answer is not *Because it pleased God to do things that way*. God of course *permitted* World War II to take place; but it was not pleasing to him.

[32] Why could a scientist not think as follows? God has created the world, and of course has created everything in it directly or indirectly. After a great deal of study, we cannot see how he created some phenomenon P (life, for example) indirectly; thus probably he has created it directly.

[33] See Aristotle, *Posterior Analytics*, bk. I, 1-4, where Aristotle declares that *scientia* is a matter of seeing what necessarily follows from what one sees to be necessarily true. (Of course Aristotle's own practice is not always easy to square with this suggestion.).

[34] Of course, this is at best a rough and general characterization: we can obviously learn of necessities *a posteriori* (for example, by using computers to prove complicated theorems) and perhaps also of contingencies *a priori*. This question of the connection between the *a priori* and the necessary, on the one hand, and the contingent and the *a posteriori* on the other (the question of the relationship between the *a priori/a posteriori* distinction and the necessary/ contingent distinction) is as deep as it is fascinating.

[35] Stek, 260-1.

PART III:

INTELLIGENT DESIGN IN SCIENCE

Chapter Five

—ᶜᵛᵛᶜ—

WHAT DOES OUR UNIVERSE REVEAL: A DESIGNER, CREATOR, OR NOTHING AT ALL?

Robert Kaita

Dr. Robert Kaita is Principal Research Physicist in the Princeton Plasma Physics Laboratory, Co-Principal Investigator for the Current Drive Experiment-Upgrade (CDX-U) and Head of Plasma Diagnostics Operations for the National Spherical Torus Experiment (NSTX). He was formerly Co-Principal Investigator for the Princeton Beta Experiment-Modified (PBX-M), one of the country's largest and most advanced tokamaks for the study of controlled thermonuclear fusion. Dr. Kaita also teaches in the graduate program in the Department of Astrophysical Sciences at Princeton University. He has been a consultant for the International Atomic Energy Agency, the U. S. Department of Energy, and the National Science Foundation, and he is a member of the American Association for the Advancement of Science, the American Physical Society, and Sigma Xi, the Scientific Research Society, where he has served as president of the Princeton Chapter.

Abstract

Modern science has been successful in explaining much of what we observe around us. The inventions it has inspired would have been considered miraculous just a short time ago. However, many fail to realize that the earliest of modern scientists were motivated by a faith that nature was comprehensible. They believed the universe was governed by the "cause-effect" laws of its Creator and this belief made science, or the search for an understanding of these laws, a rational thing to do. This essay offers personal reflections from a physicist about why science is impossible without accepting that we live in a "caused" universe that ultimately should encourage one to acknowledge its "first cause" or Creator.

"GENESIS IS A BORING BOOK." THIS statement was made by a professor at Princeton Theological Seminary.[1] Before you react to this seemingly outrageous claim, it is important to recall that our overarching goal as Christians is to engage the culture in which we live. Without this type of engagement, we will simply "talk past" those with differing views, using terms the other neither respects nor understands.

The seminary professor's assertion that Genesis is a boring book should prompt us to ask what the professor meant. The opening verses of Genesis are concise and magnificent in communicating the creation of the universe.

> In the beginning God created the heavens and the earth . . . . Then God said, "Let there be light"; and there was light . . . . and "let the dry land appear . . ."; "let the earth sprout vegetation"; let the earth bring forth living creatures"; . . . and [finally], "Let Us make man in Our image."[2]

There are no titanic struggles among the gods or stories of worlds with fantastic beings that were created and destroyed before ours. Rather, the account is "mundane" in the original and best sense of the word. It is a sober description of how the universe came to be. It certainly did not sound anachronistic when read by the Apollo 8 astronauts during a mission that epitomized the triumph of modern science.

Belief in Science and Belief in God

While the supernatural is not colorful in the Genesis account, it is evident that the only reason the "supernatural" and "natural" exist at all is because of God. As the Apostle Paul writes, "Since the creation of the world [God's] invisible attributes, His eternal power and divine nature, have been clearly seen, being understood through what has been made."[3]

For the first modern scientists, this truth made the study of His creation a rational thing to do and this is why pursuing knowledge of the physical and spiritual realms that God created remains rational today.

For the first modern scientists, this truth made the study of His creation a rational thing to do and this is why pursuing knowledge of the physical and spiritual realms that God created remains rational today.

For example, Johannes Kepler is widely admired as a great "modern" scientist, but Christian astrophysicist Owen Gingerich points out that Kepler never wavered in his "views of God as a geometer and of a universe filled with God's geometrical designs."[4] Kepler's *Astronomia Nova* includes the following exhortation:

> I implore my reader not to forget the divine goodness conferred on mankind, and which the psalmist urges him especially to consider. When he has returned from church and entered on the study of astronomy, may he praise and glorify the wisdom and greatness of the creator . . . . Let him not only extol the bounty of God in the preservation of living creatures of all kinds by the strength and stability of the earth, but also let him acknowledge the wisdom of the Creator in its motion, so abstruse, so admirable.[5]

Kepler was careful to make statements about the universe as *observations* (i.e., what the data reveal), not *proof.* While the universe clearly *reflects* the Creator, it does not necessarily prove His existence. Nonetheless, the "worldview" of the earliest modern scientists clearly reflected their belief that the Book of Laws (the Bible) tells us that the Book of Nature reveals the Creator of both. Psalm 19 testifies, "The heavens are telling of the glory of God; and their expanse is declaring the work of his hands."[6]

Therefore, the universe is not characterized by a jumble of random, unconnected phenomena, but follows ordained "Laws of Nature." This assumption made science, the search for these "Laws," a rational activity for Kepler and his contemporaries; it is implicitly assumed by all scientists today, whether or not they embrace belief in a personal Creator. I am not claiming that all, or even a majority, of scientists are theists. Even believing scientists, like myself, are rarely conscious of God's involvement in the cosmic order in our day-to-day research. All scientists implicitly assume searching for "Laws of Nature" is a rational thing to do, but the atheist may have a more difficult time explaining *why*. This is because abandoning the beliefs of Kepler and his contemporaries also requires you to abandon the reason why their approach to science is rational and purposeful. I assert that modern science actually requires "purpose" to make science possible at all.

I assert that modern science actually requires "purpose" to make science possible at all.

For example, we are practically forced to assume "purpose" to describe scientific research. Richard Feynman, the brilliant Caltech Nobel laureate physicist (known popularly as the leader of the Challenger disaster investigation), called the process analogous to learning chess by watching it being played. At first, the reasons *underlying* the variety of pieces are not obvious, and their motions seem arbitrary. After a while, however, it becomes clear that pieces of a certain type all move in the same way. There may still be occasional surprises, such as the way pawns capture pieces and become queens or the "castling" process, but the rules of the game are eventually learned from the patterns observed.[7]

This analogy helps show the value of organizing our knowledge. First, the rules in physics are simple enough that the "game" can be learned. Just as the rules of chess are finite, the equations governing the physical laws – while often difficult to solve in specific cases—are relatively few in number. For example, the gravitational, electromagnetic, and "strong and weak" nuclear forces govern all the phenomena we know in the universe.

Chess not only requires rules, but the pieces must each be the right size. If they are too small to be seen by the participants or too large to be moved by them, the game cannot be played. To illustrate this, Gingerich explains that a change of only one-half percent in the nuclear resonance levels of oxygen and carbon would have made the production of the latter impossible through stellar nucleosynthesis.[8] As a rough analogy, one could imagine the constituents of the carbon nucleus as children bouncing on trampolines near each other. We pretend the only place you find trampolines in such close proximity is the inside of stars. The object of this game is to bounce at the same frequency so that all the participants can hold hands when they are in the air. If three link hands, they call themselves "carbon," but if a fourth joins them, they become "oxygen." The "pieces" in this game have to be just the right size in order for the game to be possible.

Finally, the starting positions in chess allow us to play an interesting, (non-trivial) game. Imagine a form of chess where only two kings are placed next to each other in the middle of the board, and whoever goes first naturally wins when he captures the opponent's king. Such a game would not be interesting and would seem to have no point. Chess does not appear to be "designed" that way and neither does the universe, as evidenced by its complexity. We will revisit this in the next section.

The physical sciences are most closely associated with the "Laws of Nature" and their practitioners are the most outspoken in confronting the issue of apparent design in the universe. One way to eliminate the need for a designer, for example, is to invoke the "anthropic cosmological principle" (ACP). Hawking provides a concise statement of the ACP in his book, *A Brief History of Time*: "We see the universe the way it is because we exist…[it is as old as it is because] it takes about that long for intelligent beings to evolve."[9] This assertion was used to predict the properties of carbon and oxygen I described earlier[10] and offered as support for the validity of the ACP.

Why go to such lengths to refute "purpose," even to the point of using what may sound like a tautology? If you accept the existence of a Creator who makes science a rational endeavor, you might logically conclude that He would want to reveal Himself. The Book of Laws describes His invisible attributes, His eternal power, and divine nature.[11] This might be the sort of Creator even scientists might want to believe in, but such lofty descriptions do not force them to make the choice. The Book of Laws, however, does not stop there. It also depicts scientific details brutality of the kind that still persists, in one form or another, to the present day.

> The soldiers therefore came, and broke the legs of the first man, and of the other man who was crucified with Him, but coming to Jesus, when they saw that He was already dead, they did not break His legs; but one of the soldiers pierced His side with a spear, and immediately there came out blood and water.[12]

The account is uncomfortable because we know, scientifically, what happens when someone is crucified and then stabbed in the way the passage describes. This detail assures us that there is no doubt Jesus Christ is dead. However, this is not the end of the story. Just as science explains Christ's death, it also explains that His resurrection is impossible— unless He is the Son of God as He claimed to be.

> Then [Jesus] said to Thomas, "Reach here your finger and see My hands, and reach here your hand, and put it into My side; be not unbelieving, but believing."[13]

To engage our culture, the issue is not whether one believes in the Bible or science. One needs the Bible to understand science and one needs science to understand the Bible.

To engage our culture, the issue is not whether one believes in the Bible or science. One needs the Bible to understand science and one needs science to understand the Bible. The issue is whether one chooses to be "unbelieving" or "believing" in the face of the evidence. This seems to be why the need to challenge the "purpose" presupposition underlying science looms so large for so many today.

To summarize, I argue that "purpose" must be an underlying tenet if the pursuit of science is to be a rational activity. In addition, science, when properly understood, is an enterprise based on intelligible "rules" that are necessary to make comprehensible both the Christian faith and the "design" of the "Rulemaker." This conclusion makes some people uncomfortable and leads them to posit the "anthropic cosmological principle" (ACP) as a means by which to circumvent the "problem" of the Creator.

The Limits of Science and the Limitlessness of God

Physicists John Barrow and Frank Tipler elaborate extensively on the ACP in their book, which Nobel laureate Christian de Duve calls a "massive, vastly documented opus of 700 pages, 600 mathematical equations, and 1,500 notes and references." [14] The first of their so-called "Anthropic Statements" is straightforward:

> *Weak Anthropic Principle (WAP)*: The observed values of all physical and cosmological quantities are not equally probable but they take on values restricted by the requirements that there exist sites where carbon-based life can evolve and by the requirement that the universe be old enough for it to have already done so. [15]

In other words, this is simply an assertion "that those properties we are able to discern are self-selected by the fact that they must be consistent with our evolution and present existence."

Another physicist, Brandon Carter, first introduced a more speculative statement:

> *Strong Anthropic Principle (SAP)*: The Universe must have those properties which allow life to develop within it at some stage in its history. [16]

This goes beyond the WAP, which is cast only as a means of determining if a particular experimental observation is sensible, by placing upon the constants and laws of Nature (that is, the "rules, pieces, and initial conditions of the game") the requirement that they *must* enable life to exist. Barrow and Tipler claim that one interpretation could be categorized as "religious," in that it "continue[s] in the tradition of the classical Design Arguments" of natural theology. [17] They summarize that interpretation in the following way: "There exists one possible Universe 'designed' with the goal of generating and sustaining "observers.""[18]

We see a progression from a universe that is merely *consistent* with life, to one where it *must permit* life to develop by the sheer fact of its own existence. This may be "religious," but it certainly stands in marked contrast to the divine directedness of the universe which Genesis records as essential to its creation.

The idea of a created being that is responsible for its own creation may seem absurd, but, in the same way, some features of modern physics are used by some to provide a basis for it. Physicist, John Wheeler, offers another interpretation of the SAP. "Observers are necessary to bring the Universe into existence."[19]

Barrow and Tipler call this the Participatory Anthropic Principle (PAP) and they say it is closely related to an additional conclusion: "An ensemble of other different universes is necessary for the existence of our Universe."[20] They elaborate by adding,

> This statement receives support from the "Many Worlds" interpretation of quantum mechanics and a sum-over-histories approach to quantum gravitation because they must unavoidably recognize the existence of a whole class of *real* "other worlds" from which ours is selected by an optimizing principle.[21]

To understand what this means, let us first describe the so-called "Many Worlds" view of quantum mechanics. We use an example in physics called the two-slit diffraction experiment. In the version used by Richard Feynman, a beam of electrons impinges on a tungsten plate with two holes in it. In his colorful jargon, electrons come in "lumps" like bullets. On this microscopic level, everything looks "lumpy"—hence the appellation "quantum" mechanics for the theory that describes them. The electrons can be detected individually by any electrical system that can pick up their discrete charge. On the other hand, those that are detected past the plate follow the distribution expected if they were waves—that is, the maxima and minima characteristic of an interference pattern.[22] This is what happens when you toss pebbles into a still pond and see the ripples, which are waves of water, cross each other.

A consequence of this so-called "wave-particle duality" is the inability to determine how, as a discrete entity, the electron could be "aware" of the other hole so it can "interfere" as a wave. Furthermore, any experiment that attempts to determine which hole the electron "actually" passes through perturbs it in such a way that it indeed behaves like a bullet passing through armor plate, and does not exhibit wave-like interference.[23] It would be difficult to go into the underlying details of the quantum mechanics in this essay, but suffice it to say that, as peculiar as the theory is, you see its application every time your purchases are scanned at a cash register or a disk is popped into your CD player.

This is the great mystery of quantum mechanics. It is completely contrary to classical mechanics, where your observations are in no way contingent on the way you made it. In this framework, there is only one "reality," as reflected in the measurement you performed. In quantum mechanics, however, some hold that the two potential outcomes of the experiment with the electron reflect two possible "realities." When one of those "realities" appeared when we did our measurement, what happened to the other "reality?" The people who hold to the view of two "realities" suggest that the universe actually divides into: (a) a world that contains what we observe and (b) another whole world that "contains" the other "reality," but is forever separate and completely inaccessible to and unobservable by us. It must be this way, because we can only "experience" one reality at a time; the electron is a wave or a particle to us, but not both, when we measure its characteristics.

Such bizarre claims about the nature of "reality" are possible because there is no way to make the consequences of quantum mechanics any clearer. As the Feynman puts it,

> [H]ow does it really work? What machinery is actually producing this thing? Nobody knows any machinery. Nobody can give you a deeper explanation of this phenomenon than [what has been] given; that is, a description of it...no one can go any deeper today."[24]

Nevertheless, some have taken the idea of new "universes" being created every time a measurement is performed to establish the "Many Worlds" viewpoint,[25] which allows us creatures within the universe to create new ones by our actions in it.

We see a progression from a universe that is merely consistent with life, to one where it must permit life to develop by the sheer fact of its own existence.

Later, I address why the "Many Worlds" viewpoint might be philosophically satisfying, but, for now, I will examine why the British philosopher Mary Midgley, who is also Anglican, offers a more fundamental criticism of the PAP. The key point is that the "observer" is a disembodied physical detection device, like a photographic plate or a particle counter. An electron or a photon might behave like a particle or a wave, depending on how the measurement is performed. However, the *individual human mind* is not involved, as anybody will see the same interference pattern or a record of counts at a particular physical location for a given experimental configuration. As a result, Midgley argues:

> The vast cosmic claims collapse into absurdity. Measuring devices, if they are really detached from human intentions, are just physical objects. On their own, in a world where no mind uses or understands them, grains of silver bromide can no doubt exist and respond to photons. But they do not measure or register or record anything at all. These words only have a sense when they describe acts carried out by enquirers. The grains could indeed still be affected causally by quantum events. But then so would other physical things, for instance the particles surrounding those events. None of these effects would have any meaning, any significance, any importance. None could possibly be credited with exciting roles in creating the cosmos.[26]

If, during this discussion, your intuition suggested to you that the "Many Worlds" line of reasoning was rather incredible, you are certainly in good company. Barrow and Tipler venture an explanation as to why anyone would go to such great lengths to subscribe to the Strong Anthropic Principle (SAP) in spite of such critiques:

> Suppose that for some unknown reason the SAP is true and that intelligent life must come into existence at some stage in the Universe's history. But if it dies out at our stage of development, long before it has had any measurable non-quantum influence on the Universe in the large, it is hard to see why it must have come into existence in the first place. This motivates the following generalization of the SAP: Final Anthropic Principle (FAP): Intelligent information-processing must come into existence in the Universe, and, once it comes into existence, it will never die out.[27]

Barrow and Tipler claim that the "FAP is a statement of physics and hence *ipso facto* has no ethical or moral content."[28] In fact, it is *very much* a philosophical statement which hopes the universe does not have a designer, even though it appears as if it had one (the SAP). Yet–because the universe *has* to possess intelligent life embodied in humanity— sentient life has to go on forever. This conundrum resembles the covert question many agnostics ask: Given all that we are able to experience, feel, and do, doesn't it seem that there *must* be a point to our existence beyond an ignominious return to dust?

The best explanation Barrow and Tipler offer is to equate the meaning of existence with immortality. They "prove" the latter, and thus the "point" of intelligent life amounts to this:

1) Any living creature is fundamentally a type of computer.
2) In a computer, the program is really important, not the hardware on which it runs.
3) Humans may very well become extinct, but intelligent programs do not have to run on the "special hardware" of their bodies.

4) Intelligent "life" can thus continue to exist forever as long as there
is some type of construction material for the computer hardware,
and the energy to run them.[29]

They argue for an immortal "soul," in the sense that Aristotle and
Aquinas thought of it. I should point out that Barrow and Tipler still
refer to an individual soul, not a "world" soul. The particular claim
by Aristotle that they cite, for example, is his assertion that "soul is
analogous to knowledge possessed rather than the act of knowing. That
is, the soul is analogous to the [computer] program rather than to the
running of the program," in modern parlance.[30]

Concerning Aquinas, Barrow and Tipler point out that he

> regarded the human mind as consisting of two
> faculties: the agent intellect (intellectus agens), and the
> receptive intellect (intellectus possibilis). The former is
> the ability to acquire concepts, and the latter is the
> ability to retain and use the acquired concepts. A
> similar distinction is made in computer theory. In any
> physical computer, general rules concerning the
> processing of information are coded in the physical
> structure of the central processor and in ROM. Such
> 'hardwired' programs are analogous to Aquinas' agent
> intellect. The programs which are coded in RAM or in
> disks or tape are the computer analogue of Aquinas'
> receptive intellect.[31]

As individual computer programs exist, so can there be individual
souls. The key point is that if they are indeed equivalent, we can eliminate
God as the soul-giver who "breathed into [Adam's] nostrils the breath of
life" (Gen. 2:7, NASB), and all the consequences that follow from such
a belief.

We need not condescendingly critique the proponents of such
views, especially since those cited here are world-class scholars. Instead,
we should realize that our yearnings are the same and this should
embolden us in our witness. Helping our culture admit this is the first
and most critical step in moving from unbelief to belief, or from the

SCIENCE: CHRISTIAN PERSPECTIVES FOR THE NEW MILLENNIUM

"darken[ed] counsel by words without knowledge" (Job 38:1, NASB) to the true "Light of the World."

The Conflict of Worldviews

Contrary to popular belief, modern physics is not antithetical to a theistic perspective. Myths have given way to the explanations of science. The stories of the ancients at least present arguments of cause and effect that we can follow. As we have shown, however, the world of quantum mechanics is so contradictory to everyday experience that it becomes difficult to use in refuting any beliefs that purportedly defy "conventional" scientific wisdom. Rather, modern physics confronts us with the limitations of "science"—that we can know anything for sure. The issue is not what unique worldview permits the "impartial judgment" of science, but which among many it now permits should you choose.

Contrary to popular belief, modern physics is not antithetical to a theistic perspective.

Recall that on the scale of atomic phenomena, there are two possible outcomes to certain kinds of experiments and neither can be determined beforehand. For example, in certain quantum mechanical experiments, the *momentum* of an electron, may be tracked, but we cannot be certain of its *location*. On the other hand, if we track the location of the electron, we cannot know its momentum. There are some who believe the universe actually divides into one world that "contains" what we observe, and another world that is forever separate and unobservable, to us. This "Many Worlds" view allows us as "creatures" in the universe to "create" new realities by our actions within it.[32]

We must be reminded that what are "observing" in this paradigm is some kind of physical detection device, like a photographic plate or a particle counter. While an electron or a photon might behave like a particle or a wave, depending on how the experiment is set up, the *individual human mind* does not participate in the same manner.

Otherwise, you would be forced to claim that *everyone would not necessarily see the same physical results of a given measurement at a particular physical location for a specific experimental configuration.* This would have rather serious consequences, to say the least, for the efficacy of the scientific method. In spite of the fact that then "the vast cosmic claims collapse into absurdity," as Midgley pointed out above, the "Many Worlds" concept has many adherents, for reasons which are more philosophical than scientific. In spite of its difficulties, the ACP in its various forms—such as the "Many Worlds" viewpoint—has strong philosophical and psychological appeal to many people. The appeal comes from its seeming ability to solve the "Creator problem." Hawking unabashedly writes:

> Einstein once asked the question: "How much choice did God have in constructing the universe?" If the no boundary proposal is correct, he had no freedom at all to choose initial conditions. He would, of course, still have had the freedom to choose the laws that the universe obeyed. This, however, may not really have been all that much of a choice; there may well be only one, or a small number, of complete unified theories, such as heterotic string theory, that are self-consistent and allow the existence of structures as complicated as human beings who can investigate the laws of the universe and ask about the nature of God.[33]

Hawking concludes with the rhetorical question, "What place, then, for a creator?" His position, however, is rooted in a philosophical "anthropic" assertion —because we exist, our "creator" somehow had no choice but to create a universe that permitted this.

In fact, the Bible *does* implicitly and explicitly explain our Creator's role. The question of who (or what) has "choice" is clearly not modern. The Gospel of Luke records the joyful entry of Jesus Christ into Jerusalem, where His followers were saying, "Blessed is the King who comes in the Name of the Lord; Peace in heaven and glory in the highest!" (Luke 19:38) When the leaders of the community told Jesus to rebuke His disciples, He replied "I tell you, if these become silent, the stones will cry out!" (Luke 19:40) Contrary to what adherents of the ACP might assert, then, God does have a choice. It should humble us to realize that even stones would cry out, "What place, then, for a creator?" if we did not exist to ask the question!

Contrary to what adherents of the ACP might assert, then, God does have a choice. It should humble us to realize that even stones would cry out ... if we did not exist to ask the question!

Even if the "anthropic" explanation for the creation of the universe were tenable, it still does not address the question of its nature after it was formed. Assume that God had no "choice" in making up the "rules" we talked about in the first section. What do they give us? We can build up quite intricate and ornate objects like snowflakes from the laws of physics. Such systems are highly ordered, and their structures can be dictated by relatively few and simple instructions.

Living systems are generally not highly ordered in the same sense as snowflakes, but are immensely more complex. The instructions that are needed to specify them are consequently far more numerous. To illustrate this difference between order and complexity, note the highly simplified example following the arguments in Hubert Yockey's book, *Information Theory and Molecular Biology*.[34]

Consider a simple rule where you choose letters at random and keep only G's and H's. You repeat this until you have eleven, and the result has the high order of complexity in a snowflake. Therefore, it has low entropy, which commonly describes the degree of disorder of a system. If instead I ask you to choose three O's and one each of the letters D, E, G, L, S, U, V, and Y, their distribution is far more scattered among the alphabet than in the previous case. This situation has a much lower order and much higher entropy, but you can arrange the letters in this set to spell "God loves you." By contrast, the other high complexity/low entropy group contains no message at all.

The instructions in the situation with a greater number of letters are more complex, and so is their execution. Some claim low entropy argues for the existence of a creator, but we see how easily this can be refuted by appealing to a limited set of physical laws. Ironically, the opposite situation of high entropy with high complexity is needed to explain life. No simple rules can "create" the information required for life to exist. Unlike Hawking, I conclude that there is indeed a "place for a creator." The only way to refute this conclusion is to resort to statements like those made by the biologist de Duve, whose arguments were cited earlier. He asserts, "natural processes [are all that are permitted] if we wish to remain within the realm of science."[35]

The problems this claim causes for science can be illustrated in the comparison of two rock formations. One can be found in the Black Hills of South Dakota, and it is called Mount Rushmore. This huge relief of the heads of George Washington, Thomas Jefferson, Abraham Lincoln, and Theodore Roosevelt force one to conclude it was "created" by an intelligent designer since we know its sculptor, Gutzon Borglum.[36] Contrast this with the most famous geological feature in the White Mountains of New Hampshire — the "Profile," or the "Old Man of the Mountains." Nathaniel Hawthorne referred to it as the "Great Stone Face," and the formation became widely known through his short story by the same name. Hawthorne describes it this way:

> The Great Stone Face, then, was a work of Nature...
> [formed] precisely to resemble the features of a human
> countenance.... There was the broad arch of the forehead,
> a hundred feet in height; the nose, with its long bridge;
> the vast lips, which if they could have spoken, would
> have rolled their thunder accents from one end of the
> valley to the other.[37]

The two formations are similar in scale and granite composition. Each head on Mount Rushmore is about sixty feet high, and the "Great Stone Face" stands at an impressive 40 feet high. De Duve's position would permit focus only on the comparable "heap of ponderous and gigantic rocks, piled in a chaotic ruin one upon another" and demand that only the physical mechanism of how the rocks arrived there lies within the purview of science. As the "laws of physics and chemistry" operate identically at each location in telling us how rocks fall and fracture, the "created" sculpture and natural geological feature become essentially indistinguishable.

... it is thus philosophical assumptions and/or bias that cause many people to refuse to acknowledge the logical consequences of their methodological claims.

Science can tell the difference between the two rock formations, precisely because it permits us to consider their settings. This includes the ability to recognize Mount Rushmore as an intentional rendering of four American presidents. This provides the basis for its "meaning." Refusing to consider the questions of setting and purpose involves a refusal to see the meaning of what is observed, yet this is the consequence of de Duve's methodology. What forces this refusal is the *a priori* assumption that a creator does not exist. If observation does not support this claim, then it is not science. This limitation is imposed on science philosophically and it is thus philosophical assumptions and/or bias that cause many people to refuse to acknowledge the logical consequences of their methodological claims.

Conclusion

The universe does appear to reveal a designer and creator. Otherwise, this would not create the problem that requires positing something like the ACP. The issue is not how well the data are accumulated or how skillfully the argument is formulated in support of the Christian position. The key issue is the way in which people *respond* to the evidence—and this, in turn, follows the dictates of their worldviews.

The key issue is the way in which people respond to the evidence – and this, in turn, follows the dictates of their worldviews.

The problem of human response occurs even on a pedestrian level, as illustrated by the recent example of "crop circles" in Great Britain.[38] During the past few years, mysterious patterns were found in wheat fields in the form of large, distinct geometric patterns. No one observed them being formed, and speculation ran from "intelligent causes"—such as ingenious pranksters or the perennial favorite, extraterrestrial beings—to natural phenomena. Two gentlemen finally admitted responsibility, and revealed that their equipment consisted only of large versions of the stylus and string people have used to make geometric figures since antiquity. On the nights they were inspired to creativity, it did not take them very long to produce their designs, hence the difficulty in detecting them at work. In spite of this unequivocal "evidence for a creator," some insisted this did not explain *all* the crop patterns and some persisted in suggesting highly improbable natural causes (perhaps to cover embarrassment from their past advocacy of such fantasies as anything else).

Only when we provide appealing alternatives will others consider releasing their philosophical prejudices. Since we are dealing ultimately with mindset, we are reminded of the role God must play in changing it. The Westminster Confession of Faith states that it is ultimately He who must enlighten anyone "spiritually and savingly to understand the things of God."[39] The Confession explains that when those who reject the evidence for the Creator are effectually called, they come to accept it "most freely being made willing by His grace."[40] For Christians in the sciences, then, the goal of constructively engaging society is not simply to win the debate. We cannot truly do so against those without the "heart of flesh" that the Confession contrasts with the "heart of stone" God replaces in "His appointed and accepted time."[41] Rather, our ultimate calling is to join all believers in proclaiming the good news of salvation through Jesus Christ and the meaning this gives to our lives. That is something science alone can never provide.

---

1 Wright, D.,1993, personal communication.
2 Genesis 1:1-26 (NAS).
3 Romans 1:20 (NAS).

4 Gingerich, O., "Is There a Role for Natural Theology Today?" in *Science and Theology: Questions at the Interface*, ed. M. Rae, H. Regan, J. Stenhouse. (Edinburgh: T. and T. Clarke, 1994): 45.

5 Kepler, cited by Gingerich, 1994, 45.

6 Psalm 19:1 (NAS).

7 Feynman, R., *The Character of Physical Law*. (Cambridge, MA: MIT Press, 1967): 59-60.

8 Gingerich, O., "Let There Be Light: Modern Cosmogony and Biblical Creation" in *The World Treasury of Physics, Astronomy, and Mathematics*, ed. T. Ferris. (Boston: Little, Brown, and Co., 1991): 392.

9 Hawking, S., *A Brief History of Time* (New York: Bantam,1988): 124.

10 Hoyle, F., D. N. F. Dunbar, W. A. Wensel, and W. Whaling, *Physical Review*, 92, 1953, 1095.

11 Romans 1:20.

12 John 19:32-34 (NAS).

13 John 20:27 (NAS).

14 de Duve, C., *Vital Dust: The Origin and Evolution of Life on Earth*. (New York: Basic Books,1995): 289.

15 Barrow, J.D., and F. J. Tipler, *The Anthropic Cosmological Principle*. (Oxford: Oxford University Press,1988): 16.

16 Ibid.

17 Ibid.

18 Ibid.

19 Ibid.

20 Ibid.

21 Ibid.

22 Feynman, R., 130-137.

23 Ibid.,138-142.

24 Ibid.,145.

25 Barrow and Tipler, 21.

26 Midgely, M., *Science as Salvation: A Modern Myth and Its Meaning*. (London: Routledge,1992): 208.

27 Barrow and Tipler, 23.

28 Ibid.

29 Ibid.

30 Ibid.

31 Ibid.

32 Barrow and Tipler, 22.

33 Hawking, 1974.

34 Yockey, H.P., *Information Theory and Molecular Biology*. (Cambridge: Cambridge University Press,1992): 244.

35 de Duve, C., "The Beginnings of Life on Earth," *American Scientist* 83(5): 428.

36 Caswell, J. E., "Mount Rushmore National Memorial," *Encyclopedia Britannica*, 1968 ed., 15: 962.

37 "The Great Stone Face," *The Complete Novels and Selected Tales of Nathaniel Hawthorne* (New York: Random House, 1937): 1171.

38 Nickell, J., "Crop Cycle Mania Wanes: An Investigative Update," *Skeptical Inquirer*, 19(1995): 41-43

39 Williamson, G. I., The Westminster Confession of Faith for Study Classes. (Philadelphia: Presbyterian and Reformed Publishing Company, 1964): 88.

40 Ibid.

41 Ibid.

Chapter Six

———

DOES RECENT SCIENTIFIC EVIDENCE SUPPORT AN INTELLIGENTLY DESIGNED UNIVERSE?

WITH AUDIENCE DISCUSSION

Walter L. Bradley

Dr. Walter L. Bradley is currently Distinguished Professor of Engineering at Baylor University. Prior to that, Professor Bradley was on the faculty at Texas A&M University for 24 years, where he served in the department and as department head of the largest Mechanical Engineering Department in the country and as Director of the university's Polymer Technology Center.

Professor Bradley has published over 145 technical articles and book chapters. His research accomplishments were recognized by being elected as a Fellow of the American Society for Materials and the American Scientific Affiliation. His teaching abilities were recognized by receiving two university-wide teaching awards. Dr. Bradley has given a lecture entitled, "Is There Scientific Evidence for the Existence of God?" to over 65,000 college students on 70 university campuses.

Abstract

Our universe is such a remarkable place of habitation for complex, conscious life that it is extremely difficult to believe it is the result of a series of cosmic accidents. The elegant mathematic forms encoded in nature, the nineteen universal constants that are exactly what they must be, and the multitude of initial conditions argue persuasively for a universe that has been carefully crafted for our benefit.

WHAT DOES IT MEAN ON A GRAND SCALE to assert that the universe is the product of an intelligent designer? In a scientific age that exalts rationalism and chance, what empirical evidence could possibly support such a claim? As humans contemplating the immense complexity of the cosmos, might certain features of the universe suggest that our "home" has in fact been carefully crafted for our benefit? Can our own human experiences of creativity and design illuminate the concept of a cosmic designer? These questions underlie the discussion of intelligent design theory, a resurgent area of inquiry by both Christian and secular scientists in search of a reasonable explanation for the marvelous complexity of the universe.

What Is "an Intelligently Designed Universe"?

In his classic, *Natural Theology* (1802),[1] eighteenth-century English philosopher and theologian William Paley marshaled evidence for a designed universe from both the physical and biological sciences. However, his argument for design was called into question by Darwin's theory of evolution. But new discoveries in the latter half of the twentieth century in the fields of astronomy, cosmology, and abiogenesis (the origin of life) have provided extremely compelling evidence for a designed universe. These findings have been publicized in the popular print media (*Time*, December 1992 and *Newsweek*, July 1998), featured in television specials on PBS and BBC, and disseminated through a wide variety of popular and scholarly books, including entries from prestigious academic publishing houses such as Oxford and Cambridge University Presses.

My personal experience as a lecturer supports the growing openness to intelligent design theory in the academic world. Having given over 135 talks on this subject to more than 65,000 students and professors at over 65 major university campuses from 1986 to 2002, I have observed a dramatic change in audience receptivity to the idea that an intelligent designer of the universe may exist. I have noted a widespread acceptance (albeit begrudging in some quarters) that this growing body of scientific evidence demands an intellectually honest reckoning, as no exclusively naturalistic explanation seems capable of rising to the occasion.

Before we examine the evidence from cosmology, physics, and chemistry that suggests the universe has been designed as an ideal habitat for life in general and for humans in particular, let me first clarify what is meant by the term "design."

Identifying Designed Objects in the Natural World

Richard Dawkins, a British zoologist and one of the world's foremost apologists for classical Darwinism, addressed the question of design in his 1996 essay collection, *Climbing Mount Improbable*,[2] by contrasting particular, designed artifacts with similar accidents in nature. Dawkins illustrates the concept of design with the example of Mount Rushmore, upon which are carved the clearly recognizable images of Presidents Washington, Jefferson, Lincoln and Theodore Roosevelt (*Figure 1*). By contrast, a naturally occurring rock in Hawaii casts a shadow that resembles President John F. Kennedy (*Figure 2*), illustrating an accidental occurrence in nature. It is self-evident that a sculptor (in this case, Gutzon Borglum) carved Mount Rushmore. The sheer number of details in which the Mount Rushmore faces resemble the faces of the four presidents testifies to the presence of an intelligent cause, a human sculptor. No one could seriously attribute these magnificent faces to the creative forces of wind, rain, sleet, and hail.

The first step in evaluating the possibility of intelligent design is to examine closely the characteristics (or artifacts) of the natural world in order to assess whether all external "appearances" of design are merely "designoids," or true examples of design by an intelligent Creator.

Dawkins defines *designoids* as artifacts of the natural world that appear to be designed but "have in fact been shaped by a magnificently non-random process which creates an almost perfect illusion of design."[3] A *designoid* is an artifact in nature that looks like Mount Rushmore but can in fact be explained by natural processes (with, say, natural selection being the non-random process in the case of living systems).

The first step in evaluating the possibility of intelligent design is to examine closely the characteristics (or artifacts) of the natural world in order to assess whether all external "appearances" of design are merely "designoids," or true examples of design by an intelligent Creator. Let us begin by considering the essential elements of intelligent design by human beings.

Figure 1 *An intelligent design: Mount Rushmore with presidents Washington, Jefferson, Roosevelt, and Lincoln.*

Figure 2 *An accident of nature: President John F. Kennedy's profile formed by shadow cast by a large rock in Hawaii.*[2]

How an Engineer Designs Something

Design engineers using their understanding of natural laws, as described by mathematics, and their capacity to prescribe the conditions under which these natural laws function locally to produce a purposeful outcome. Let me illustrate. Suppose I wanted to throw a water balloon from the leaning Tower of Pisa in Italy to hit a friend walking on the plaza below. Solving the differential equation that Newton discovered for motion in a gravitational field, I would obtain a solution in the form of a simple, algebraic equation that describes the descent of the water balloon to its target below.

$$H(t) = h_0 - (Gm/r^2)\, t^2/2 - \upsilon_0 t \tag{1}$$

Here "H(t)" represents the height of the balloon as a function of time ("t"); "G" is a universal constant signifying the strength of the gravitational force of attraction; "m" and "r" are the mass of the Earth and the radius of the Earth, respectively; and "h_0" and "v_0" are the height of the tower from which I shall throw the balloon and the vertical velocity with which I shall throw the balloon, respectively. By entering the numerical values for "G," "m," and "r," I obtain $Gm/r^2 = 32.2$ ft/s^2, usually designated "g." Now Equation 1 can be simplified to:

$$H (t) = h_0 - g\, t^2 / 2\ -\ v_0\, t\ = h_0 - 32.2\, t^2 / 2 - v_0\, t \tag{2}$$

I can now solve Equation 2 for the time "t" it will take for the water balloon to reach the ground [H(t) = 0] if I specify the height of the tower [h_0] and the initial velocity [v_0] with which the water balloon is thrown. This equation may be used to guarantee that my balloon arrives at the plaza at just the right time to hit my strolling friend. Simply dropping the balloon will also accomplish my goal. I specify $v_0 = 0$ and H(t) = 0 and solve for the correct time to drop the balloon.

Human Design Sets Boundary Conditions

These three essential factors to predict the motion of my water balloon are the same ones generally necessary to achieve design outcomes in engineering. They are:

- the mathematical form that nature takes (see *Equations 1 and 2*);
- the values of the universal constants (G in *Equation 1*) and local constants (the radius of Earth, r, and the mass of the Earth, m, in *Equation 1*); and
- the boundary conditions (the height [h_0] and initial velocity [v_0] in this example.

Note that the engineer has no control over the laws of nature and the mathematical forms they assume. Neither does the engineer have any control over the values of the universal constants, such as the gravity force constant. The engineer can only set the boundary conditions; for example, when drawing up blueprints to specify exactly how a device will look and operate when it has been manufactured.

If we revisit the design process, this time using the more realistic—though complex—example of automobile design, the engineer must carefully prescribe the boundary conditions such that the chemical energy released by the internal combustion of gasoline is converted into mechanical energy in the form of torque to the car wheels. Furthermore, the dimensions for each engine part are of critical importance. The absolute size and shape of each part is determined by the car's desired weight, speed, passenger and luggage capacity, and other performance specifications. These factors determine the size of the engine cylinders and pistons and the rate of gasoline injected into the engine cylinders, the scale of the brake and suspension systems, the size and type of tires, and so forth. And whatever their absolute characteristics, the parts chosen must also be scaled in relationship to one another so that they can work together harmoniously.

Notice that many of the specifications are related to each other and therefore cannot be independently specified or assigned. The greater this interdependence of specified boundary conditions, the more complex and demanding is the design process. Small errors in the specification of any such requirement will produce either a car with very poor performance or, worse, a car that does not function at all.

Small errors in the specification of any such requirement will produce either a car with very poor performance or, worse, a car that does not function at all.

In summary, we can see that human design consists in specification of conditions under which the laws of nature operate to produce a purposeful outcome. In the next section, we will see that cosmic design involves specification of not only the conditions under which the laws of nature operate, but the laws themselves and the universe constants that scale the "building blocks" (e.g., rest masses of elemental particles), "energy blocks" (e.g., quanta of energy), and the fundamental forces in nature to provide the purposeful outcome of a habitable universe for life, and life itself!

Designing the Blueprint for a Habitable Universe

We teach mechanical engineering students to begin the design process by specifying as clearly as possible the "needs statement" for their project. Then, the assignment for the semester is to develop a design solution that accomplishes the "need(s)" specified for the project. In similar fashion, the minimal needs to be satisfied for a universe to be capable of supporting life of any imaginable type, not just life as we know it, must be identified. Like our automobile illustration, many of the specifications will necessarily be interrelated to make a functional universe. From this essential "needs statement" we can then see how these needs (or design requirements) are met in our universe. We are essentially doing reverse engineering, constructing the blueprint backwards from the product (like an illicit manufacturing company copying a competitor's product). Only then will we be ready to entertain Dawkins' question, "Are there many ways in which these requirements could be satisfied within nature?"[4] Or are the conditions so unique and interrelated that their collective satisfaction by accident would be a "miracle" in its own right? Let us then begin by drafting a "needs statement" for a habitable universe. Then we shall see how these requirements are satisfied in our universe.

Designing the Needs Statement for a Habitable Universe

An abbreviated list of requirements for a universe suitable to support life of any imaginable type must include the following items:

- *Order* to provide the stable environment that is conducive to the development of life, but with *just enough chaotic behavior* to provide a driving force for change.
- *Sufficient chemical stability and elemental diversity* to build the complex molecules necessary for essential life functions: processing energy, storing information, and replicating. A universe of just hydrogen and helium will not "work."
- *Predictability in chemical reactions*, allowing compounds to form from the various elements.

- A *"universal connector,"* an element that is essential for the molecules of life. It must have the chemical property that permits it to react readily with almost all other elements, forming bonds that are stable, but not too stable, so disassembly is also possible. Carbon is the only element in our periodic chart that satisfies this requirement.

- A *"universal solvent"* in which the chemistry of life can unfold. Since chemical reactions are too slow in the solid state, and complex life would not likely be sustained as a gas, there is a need for a liquid element or compound that readily dissolves both the reactants and the reaction products essential to living systems: namely, a liquid with the properties of water.

- A *stable source of energy to sustain living systems* in which there must be photons from the sun with sufficient energy to drive organic, chemical reactions, but not so energetic as to destroy organic molecules (as in the case of highly energetic ultraviolet radiation).

- A *means of transporting the energy* from the source (like our sun) to the place where chemical reactions occur in the solvent (like water on Earth) must be available. In the process, there must be minimal losses in transmission if the energy is to be utilized efficiently.

Unless ALL these conditions, and many more not included in this list, are met, we would have a universe that would preclude the possibility of conscious, complex life forms.

Unless *ALL* these conditions, and many more not included in this list, are met, we would have a universe that would preclude the possibility of conscious, complex life forms. However, it is possible to meet all of these conditions for the universe and still not necessarily find a suitable habitat in the universe for complex, conscious life. Therefore, we might say that the above requirements for our universe are necessary conditions, but not by themselves sufficient, for a habitat suitable for complex human life. Next we try to identify the additional conditions within such a suitable universe that would provide a place of habitation for conscious, complex life.

Designing the Needs Statement for a Habitable Place in a Universe Suitable for Life

An abbreviated, but illustrative, list of additional requirements must be specified for a place of habitation in this universe. First, we need a star that is located in a relatively "quiet" region of the universe (e.g., not too many neighbors that are producing high intensity, sterilizing radiation). This star needs to have its highest intensity of radiation in the range that is suitable to drive the chemical reactions essential to life without destroying the products of these reactions. Furthermore, this star needs to have a very special satellite within its solar system. A partial list of the requirements this satellite must meet include:

- planet or moon that is terrestrial—or, solid rather than gaseous;
- temperature range suitable to maintain the universal solvent as a liquid rather than a solid or gas;
- just the right concentration of heavy (radioactive) elements to heat the core of the planet and provide the necessary energy to drive plate tectonics, to build up land mass in what would otherwise be a smooth, round planet completely covered with solvent;
- just the right amount of solvent (carefully coupled to the plate tectonics activity) to provide a planet with similar proportions of its surfaces as oceans and land mass;
- just the right protection from the destructive forces in nature such as radiation and asteroids over a reasonable amount of time; and
- just the right stabilized axis tilt and angular velocity to give moderate, regular, and predictable seasons and moderate temperature fluctuations from day to night.

While one is tempted to think that these requirements are easily met, given the large number of stars, it should be noted that there are few places in the universe sufficiently free of sterilizing radiation to provide a suitable solar system. The number of candidate "neighborhoods" is further reduced by the requirements of a sun with the right amount of mass to give the right electromagnetic radiation spectrum. Furthermore, the occurrence of a suitable satellite in conjunction with such a star is even more problematic. Only the earth in our solar system of sixty-two satellites meets the above requirements for a "home" (earth) in a safe "neighborhood" like our sun and solar system, which are well placed in a quiet place in a suitable universe as described above.

In the next sections, we will see how these universal and local "needs" (or design requirements) are met by: the specific mathematical form encoded in nature, the exact values of the universal constants in our universe, and the remarkable "coincidence" that initial (or boundary) conditions are exactly what they must be. We will also see that the "evolutionary" or developmental path that our universe navigated is consistently remarkable, making the origin of our "Garden of Eden" all the more wondrous and enigmatic.

Design: Mathematics and the Deep Structure of the Universe

Mathematics—in contrast to mere calculation—is an abstract intellectual activity that began in Greece in the sixth century BC. Pythagoras was a key figure, as were his successors, Euclid and Archimedes. Their studies focused especially on geometric objects such as straight lines, circles, ellipses, and conic sections (i.e., the curves made by cutting a cone with a plane).

In the third century BC, Appolonius of Perga wrote eight monumental volumes devoted to these curves, describing their properties as "miraculous." Yet the geometric and mathematical formulations to which they devoted themselves were actually descriptions encoded into the very fabric of nature. Imagine the delight of Johannes Kepler (1571–1630) some eighteen centuries later, when he discovered that the orbits of planets around the sun conformed to these same beautiful but abstract mathematical forms. Kepler declared: "The chief aim of all investigations of the external world should be to discover the rational order and harmony which has been imposed on it by God and which He revealed to us in the language of mathematics."[5]

Galileo Galilei (1564–1642) asserted "the laws of nature are written by the hand of God in the language of mathematics."[6] In his *Mathematics: The Loss of Certainty,*[7] historian Morris Kline demonstrates that the religious mathematicians of the sixteenth and seventeenth centuries—including Newton, Galileo, Kepler, and Copernicus—viewed the universe as orderly and capable of mathematical description precisely because a rational God had fashioned it thus. These scientist-mathematicians believed that, since God had designed the universe, then "all phenomena of nature would follow one master plan. One mind designing a universe would almost surely have employed one set of basic principles to govern all related phenomena."[8]

Only in the 20th century have we come to fully understand that the incredibly diverse phenomena that we observe in nature are the outworking of a very small number of physical laws, each of which may be described by a simple mathematical relationship. Indeed, so simple in mathematical form and small in number are these physical laws that they can all be written on one side of one sheet of paper, as seen in *Table 1*.

Eugene Wigner, Nobel laureate physicist, in his widely quoted paper, *The Unreasonable Effectiveness of Mathematics in the Physical Sciences,* notes that scientists often take for granted the remarkable— even miraculous—effectiveness of mathematics in describing the real world. Wigner muses:

> The enormous usefulness of mathematics is something bordering on the mysterious . . . . There is no rational explanation for it . . . . The miracle of the appropriateness of the language of mathematics for the formulation of the laws of physics is a wonderful gift which we neither understand nor deserve.[9]

Albert Einstein was struck by the wondrous orderliness of the world as he explains below:

> You find it strange that I consider the comprehensibility of the world (to the extent that we are authorized to

speak of such a comprehensibility) as a miracle or as an eternal mystery. Well, *a priori*, one should expect a chaotic world, which cannot be grasped by the mind in any way.... [T]he kind of order created by Newton's theory of gravitation, for example, is wholly different. Even if man proposes the axioms of the theory, the success of such a project presupposes a high degree of ordering of the objective world, and this could not be expected *a priori*. That is the "miracle" which is being constantly reinforced as our knowledge expands.[10]

Table 1
The Fundamental Laws of Nature

- Mechanics (Hamilton's Equations)

$$\dot{p} = -\frac{\partial H}{\partial q} \qquad \dot{q} = -\frac{\partial H}{\partial p}$$

- Electrodynamics (Maxwell's Equations)

$$F^{\mu\nu} = \partial^\mu A^\nu - \partial^\nu A^\mu$$

$$\partial_\mu F^{\mu\nu} = j^\nu$$

- Statistical Mechanics (Boltzmann's Equations)

$$S = -k \int f \log f \, d\upsilon$$

$$\frac{dS}{dt} \geq 0$$

- Quantum Mechanics (Schrödinger's Equations)

$$I\hbar|\dot{\psi}\rangle = H|\psi\rangle$$

$$\Delta X \Delta P \geq \frac{\hbar}{2}$$

- General Relativity (Einstein's Equation)
  $$G_{\mu\upsilon} = -8\pi G T_{\mu\upsilon}$$

Yet, even the splendid orderliness of the cosmos, expressible in the mathematical forms seen in Table 1, is only a small first step in creating a universe with a suitable place for habitation by complex, conscious life. The particulars of the mathematical forms themselves are also critical. Consider the problem of stability at the atomic and cosmic levels. Both Hamilton's equations for non-relativistic, Newtonian mechanics and Einstein's theory of general relativity (see Table 1) are unstable for a sun with planets unless the gravitational potential energy is proportional to r^{-1}, a requirement that is only met for a universe with three spatial dimensions. For Schrödinger's equations for quantum mechanics to give stable, bound energy levels for atomic hydrogen (and by implication, for all atoms), the universe must have no more than three spatial dimensions. Maxwell's equations for electromagnetic energy transmission also require that the universe be no more than three-dimensional.

Richard Courant illustrates this felicitous meeting of natural laws with the example of sound and light: "[O]ur actual physical world, in which acoustic or electromagnetic signals are the basis of communication, seems to be singled out among the mathematically conceivable models by intrinsic simplicity and harmony."[11]

To summarize, for life to exist, we need an orderly (and by implication, intelligible) universe. Order at many different levels is required. For instance, to have planets that circle their stars, we need Newtonian mechanics operating in a three-dimensional universe. For there to be multiple stable elements of the periodic table to provide a sufficient variety of atomic "building blocks" for life, we need atomic structure to be constrained by the laws of quantum mechanics. We further need the orderliness in chemical reactions that is the consequence of Boltzmann's equation for the second law of thermodynamics. And for an energy source like the sun to transfer its life-giving energy to a habitat like Earth, we require the laws of electromagnetic radiation that Maxwell described.

Many modern scientists, like mathematicians centuries before them, have been awestruck by the evidence for intelligent design implicit in nature's mathematical harmony and the internal consistency of the laws of nature.

Our universe is indeed orderly, and in precisely the way necessary for it to serve as a suitable habitat for life. The wonderful internal ordering of the cosmos is matched only by its extraordinary economy. Each one of the fundamental laws of nature is essential to life itself. A universe lacking any of the laws shown in *Table 1* would almost certainly be a universe without life. Many modern scientists, like mathematicians centuries before them, have been awestruck by the evidence for intelligent design implicit in nature's mathematical harmony and the internal consistency of the laws of nature. Australian astrophysicist Paul Davies declares:

> All the evidence so far indicates that many complex structures depend most delicately on the existing form of these laws. It is tempting to believe, therefore, that a complex universe will emerge only if the laws of physics are very close to what they are....The laws, which enable the universe to come into being spontaneously, seem themselves to be the product of exceedingly ingenious design. If physics is the product of design, the universe must have a purpose, and the evidence of modern physics suggests strongly to me that the purpose includes us.[12]

British astronomer Sir Fred Hoyle likewise comments,

> I do not believe that any scientist who examines the evidence would fail to draw the inference that the laws of nuclear physics have been deliberately designed with regard to the consequences they produce inside stars. If this is so, then my apparently random quirks have

> become part of a deep-laid scheme. If not, then we are
> back again at a monstrous sequence of accidents.[13]

Nobel laureates Eugene Wigner and Albert Einstein have respectfully evoked "mystery" or "eternal mystery" in their meditations upon the brilliant mathematical encoding of nature's deep structures. But as Kepler, Newton, Galileo, Copernicus, Davies, and Hoyle and many others have noted, the mysterious coherency of the mathematical forms underlying the cosmos is solved if we recognize these forms to be the creative intentionality of an intelligent creator who has purposefully designed our cosmos as an ideal habitat for us.

Design: Universal Constants or Cosmic Coincidences?

Next, let us turn to the deepest level of cosmic harmony and coherence—that of the elemental forces and universal constants which govern all of nature. Much of the essential design of our universe is embodied in the scaling of the various forces, such as gravity and electromagnetism, and the sizing of the rest mass of the various elemental particles such as electrons, protons, and neutrons.

There are certain universal constants that are indispensable for our mathematical description of the universe (see *Table 2*). These include Planck's constant, h; the speed of light, c; the gravity-force constant, G; the rest masses of the proton, electron, and neutron; the unit charge for the electron or proton; the weak force, strong nuclear force, electromagnetic coupling constants; and Boltzmann's constant, k.

Table 2
Universal Constants

- Speed of light $\quad\quad\quad$ c $\quad = 3.0 \times 10^8$ m/s
- Planck's constant $\quad\quad$ h $\quad = 6.63 \times 10^{-34}$ J-s
- Boltzmann's constant $\quad$ k $\quad = 1.38 \times 10^{-23}$ J/$^\circ$K
- Unit charge $\quad\quad\quad\quad$ q $\quad = 1.6 \times 10^{-19}$ Coulombs
- Rest mass proton $\quad\quad$ m_p $= 1.67 \times 10^{-27}$ kg
- Rest mass of neutron $\quad$ m_n $= 1.69 \times 10^{-27}$ kg
- Rest mass of electron $\quad$ m_e $= 9.11 \times 10^{-31}$ kg
- Gravity force constant $\quad$ G $\quad = 6.67 \times 10^{-11}$ N-m^2/kg^2

When cosmological models were first developed in the mid-twentieth century, cosmologists naively assumed that the selection of a given set of constants was not critical to the formation of a suitable habitat for life. Through subsequent parametric studies that varied those constants, scientists now know that relatively small changes in any of the constants produce a dramatically different universe and one that is not hospitable to life of any imaginable type.

The "just so" nature of the universe has fascinated both scientists and laypersons, giving rise to a flood of titles such as *The Anthropic Cosmological Principle*,[14] *Universes*,[15] *The Accidental Universe*,[16] *Superforce*,[17] *The Cosmic Blueprint*,[18] *Cosmic Coincidences*,[19] *The Anthropic Principle*,[20] *Universal Constants in Physics*,[21] *The Creation Hypothesis*,[22] and *Mere Creation: Science, Faith and Intelligent Design*.[23] Let us examine several examples from a longer list of approximately one hundred requirements that constrain the selection of the universal constants to a remarkable degree.

Twentieth-century physicists have identified four fundamental forces in nature. These may each be expressed as dimensionless numbers to allow a comparison of their relative strengths. These values vary by a factor of 10^{41} (10 with forty additional zeros after it), or by 41 orders of magnitude. Yet modest changes in the relative strengths of any of these forces and their associated constants would produce dramatic changes in the universe, rendering it unsuitable for life of any imaginable type. Several examples to illustrate this fine-tuning of our universe are presented next.

Design: Balancing Electromagnetism and Gravity Forces

The electromagnetic force is 10^{38} times stronger than the gravity force. Gravity draws hydrogen into stars, creating a high-temperature plasma. The protons in the plasma must overcome their electromagnetic repulsion to fuse. Thus, the relative strength of the gravity force to the electromagnetic force determines the rate at which stars "burn" by fusion. If this ratio of strengths were altered to 10^{32} instead of 10^{38} (i.e., if gravity were much stronger), stars would be a billion times less massive and would burn a million times faster.[24]

Electromagnetic radiation and the light spectrum also depend on the relative strengths of the gravity and electromagnetic forces and their associated constants. Furthermore, the frequency distribution of electromagnetic radiation produced by the sun must be precisely tuned to the energies of the various chemical bonds on Earth. Excessively energetic photons of radiation (i.e., the ultraviolet radiation emitted from a blue giant star) destroy chemical bonds and destabilize organic molecules. Insufficiently energetic photons (e.g., infrared and longer wavelength radiation from a red dwarf star) would result in chemical reactions that are either too sluggish or would not occur at all. All life on Earth depends upon fine-tuned solar radiation, which requires, in turn, a very precise balancing of the electromagnetic and gravitational forces.

As previously noted, the chemical bonding energy relies upon quantum mechanical calculations that include the electromagnetic force, the mass of the electron, the speed of light (c), and Planck's constant (h). Matching the radiation from the sun to the chemical bonding energy requires that the magnitude of six constants be selected to satisfy the following inequality, with the caveat that the two sides of the inequality are of the same order of magnitude, guaranteeing that the photons are sufficiently energetic, but not too energetic.[25]

$$m_p^2 \, G/[hc] > \tilde{} \, [e^2/\{hc\}]^{12} [m_e/m_p]^4 \qquad (3)$$

Substituting the values in Table 2 for h, c, G, me, mp, and e (with units adjusted as required) allows Equation 3 to be evaluated to give:

$$5.9 \times 10^{-39} > 2.0 \times 10^{-39} \qquad (4)$$

In what is either an amazing coincidence or careful design by an intelligent Creator, these constants have the very precise values relative to each other that are necessary to give a universe in which radiation from the sun is tuned to the necessary chemical reactions that are essential for life.

In what is either an amazing coincidence or careful design by an intelligent Creator, these constants have the very precise values relative to each other that are necessary to give a universe in which radiation from the sun is tuned to the necessary chemical reactions that are essential for life. This result is illustrated in Figure 3, where the intensity of radiation from the sun and the biological utility of radiation are shown as a function of the wavelength of radiation. The greatest intensity of radiation from the sun occurs at the place of greatest biological utility.

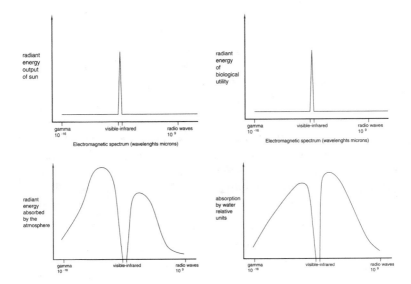

Figure 3 *The visible portion of the electromagnetic spectrum (~1 micron) is the most intense radiation from the sun (upper, left); has the greatest biological utility (upper, right); and passes through atmosphere of Earth (lower, left) and water (lower, right) with almost no absorption. It is uniquely this same wavelength of radiation that is idea to foster the chemistry of life. This is either a truly amazing series of coincidences or else the result of careful design.*

Happily, our star (the sun) emits radiation (light) that is finely tuned to drive the chemical reactions necessary for life. But there is still a critical potential problem: getting that radiation from the sun to the place where the chemical reactions occur. Passing through the near vacuum of space is no problem. However, absorption of light by either

Earth's atmosphere or by water where the necessary chemical reactions occur could render life on Earth impossible. It is remarkable that both the Earth's atmosphere and water have "optical windows" that allow visible light (just the radiation necessary for life) to pass through with very little absorption, whereas shorter wavelength (destructive ultraviolet radiation) and longer wavelength (infrared) radiation are both highly absorbed, as seen in *Figure 3*.[26] This allows solar energy in the form of light to reach the reacting chemicals in the universal solvent, which is water. The *Encyclopedia Britannica*[27] observes in this regard:

> Considering the importance of visible sunlight for all aspects of terrestrial life, one cannot help being awed by the dramatically narrow window in the atmospheric absorption...and in the absorption spectrum of water.

It is remarkable that the optical properties of water and our atmosphere, the chemical bonding energies of the chemicals of life, and the radiation from the sun are all precisely harmonized to allow living systems to utilize energy from the sun, without which life could not exist.

It is remarkable that the optical properties of water and our atmosphere, the chemical bonding energies of the chemicals of life, and the radiation from the sun are all precisely harmonized to allow living systems to utilize energy from the sun, without which life could not exist. It is analogous to your car, which can only run using gasoline as a fuel. Happily, but not accidentally, the service station has an ample supply of exactly the right fuel for your automobile. But someone had to drill for and produce the oil, someone had to refine it into liquid fuel (gasoline) that has been carefully optimized for your internal combustion engine, and others had to truck it to your service station. The production and transportation of the right energy from the sun for the metabolic motors of plants and animals is much more remarkable, and hardly accidental.

Finally, without this unique window of light transmission through water, which is constructed upon an intricate framework of universal constants, vision would be impossible and sight-communication would cease, since living tissue and eyes are composed mainly of water.

Design: Nuclear Strong Force and Electromagnetic Force

The nuclear strong force is the strongest force within nature, occurring at the subatomic level to bind protons and neutrons within atomic nuclei.[28] Were we to increase the ratio of the strong force to the electromagnetic force by only 3.4 percent, the result would be a universe with no hydrogen, no long-lived stars that burn hydrogen, and no water (a molecule composed of two hydrogen atoms and one oxygen atom)—our "universal solvent" for life. Likewise, a decrease of only nine percent in the strong force relative to the electromagnetic force would decimate the periodic table of elements. Such a change would prevent deuterons from forming from the combination of protons and neutrons. Deuterons, in turn, combine to form helium, then helium fuses to produce beryllium, and so forth.[29]

Within the nucleus, an even more precise balancing of the strong force and the electromagnetic force allows for a universe with an abundance of organic building blocks, including both carbon and oxygen.[30] Carbon serves as the universal connector for organic life and is an optimal reactant with almost every other element, forming bonds that are stable but not too stable, allowing compounds to be formed and disassembled. Oxygen is a component of water, the necessary universal solvent where life chemistry can occur. This is why when people speculate about life on Mars, they first look for signs of organic molecules (ones containing carbon) and signs that Mars once had water.

Quantum physics examines the most minute energy exchanges at the deepest levels of the cosmic order. Only certain energy levels are permitted within nuclei-like steps on a ladder. If the mass-energy for two colliding particles results in a combined mass-energy that is equal to or slightly less than a permissible energy level on the quantum "energy ladder," then the two nuclei will readily stick together or fuse on collision, with the energy difference needed to reach the step being supplied by the kinetic energy of the colliding particles. If this mass-energy level for the combined particles is exactly right, then the collisions are said to have resonance, which is to say that there is a high efficiency within the collision. On the other hand, if the combined mass-energy results in a value that is slightly higher than one of the permissible energy levels on the energy ladder, then the particles will simply bounce off each other rather than fusing, or sticking together.

It is clear that the step sizes between quantum nuclear energy levels depends on the balance between the strong force and the electromagnetic force, and these steps must be tuned to the mass-energy levels of various nuclei for resonance to occur and give an efficient conversion by fusion of lighter element into carbon, oxygen and heavier elements.

In 1953, Sir Fred Hoyle *et al.* predicted the existence of the unknown resonance energy level for carbon, and it was subsequently confirmed through experimentation.[31] In 1982, Hoyle offered a very insightful summary of the significance he attached to his remarkable predictions.

> From 1953 onward, Willy Fowler and I have always been intrigued by the remarkable relation of the 7.65 MeV energy level in the nucleus of 12 C to the 7.12 MeV level in 16 O. If you wanted to produce carbon and oxygen in roughly equal quantities by stellar nucleosynthesis, these are the two levels you would have to fix, and your fixing would have to be just where these levels are actually found to be. Another put-up job? Following the above argument, I am inclined to think so. A common sense interpretation of the facts suggests that a super intellect has "monkeyed" with the physics as well as the chemistry and biology, and there are no blind forces worth speaking about in nature.[32]

Design: The Rest Mass of Subatomic Particles

Scientists have been surprised to discover the extraordinary tuning of the masses of the elementary particles to each other and to the forces in nature. Stephen Hawking has noted that the difference in the rest mass of the neutron and the rest mass of the proton must be approximately equal to twice the mass of the electron. The mass-energy of the proton is 938.28 MeV and the mass-energy of the neutron is 939.57 MeV. The mass-energy of the electron is 0.51 MeV, or approximately half of the difference in neutron and proton mass-energies, just as Hawking indicated it must be.[33] If the mass-energy of the proton plus the mass-energy of the electron were not slightly smaller than the mass-energy of the neutron, then electrons would combine with protons to form neutrons, with all atomic structure collapsing, leaving an inhospitable world composed only of neutrons.

Again, a meticulous inner design assures a universe with long-term sources of energy and elemental diversity.

On the other hand, if this difference were larger, then neutrons would all decay into protons and electrons, leaving a world of pure hydrogen, since neutrons are necessary for protons to combine to build heavier nuclei and the associated elements. As things stand, the neutron is just heavy enough to ensure that the Big Bang would yield one neutron to every seven protons, allowing for an abundant supply of hydrogen for star fuel and enough neutrons to build up the heavier elements in the universe.[34] Again, a meticulous inner design assures a universe with long-term sources of energy and elemental diversity.

Design: Balancing the Nuclear Weak Coupling Force

The weak force governs certain interactions at the subatomic or nuclear level. If the weak force coupling constant were slightly larger, neutrons would decay more rapidly, reducing the production of deuterons, and thus of helium and elements with heavier nuclei. On the other hand, if the weak force coupling constant were slightly weaker, the Big Bang would have burned almost all of the hydrogen into helium, with the ultimate outcome being a universe with little or no hydrogen and many heavier elements instead. This would leave no long-lived stars and no hydrogen-containing compounds, especially water. In 1991, Breuer noted that the appropriate mix of hydrogen and helium to provide hydrogen-containing compounds, long-term stars, and heavier elements is approximately 75 percent hydrogen and 25 percent helium, which is just what we find in our universe.[35]

This is obviously only an illustrative—but not exhaustive—list of cosmic "coincidences." Clearly, the four forces in nature and the universal constants must be very carefully calibrated or scaled to provide a universe that satisfies the key requirements for life that we enumerated in our initial "needs statement": for example, elemental diversity, an abundance of oxygen and carbon, and a long-term energy source (our sun) that is precisely matched to the bonding strength of organic molecules, with minimal absorption by water or Earth's terrestrial atmosphere.

John Wheeler, formerly Professor of Physics at Princeton, in discussing these observations asks:

> Is man an unimportant bit of dust on an unimportant planet in an unimportant galaxy somewhere in the vastness of space? No! The necessity to produce life lies at the center of the universe's whole machinery and design....Slight variations in physical laws such as gravity or electromagnetism would make life impossible.[36]

Design: Critical Initial or Boundary Conditions

As we already suggested, correct mathematical forms and exactly the right values for the universal constants are necessary but not sufficient, to guarantee a suitable habitat for complex, conscious life. For all of the mathematical elegance and inner attunement of the cosmos, life still would not have occurred had not initial conditions been properly set at certain critical points in the formation of the universe and Earth. Let us briefly consider the initial conditions for the Big Bang, the design of our terrestrial "Garden of Eden," and the staggering informational requirements for the origin and development of the first living system.

For all of the mathematical elegance and inner attunement of the cosmos, life still would not have occurred had not initial conditions been properly set at certain critical points in the formation of the universe and Earth.

The Big Bang

The "Big Bang" follows the physics of any explosion, though on an inconceivably large scale. The critical boundary condition for the Big Bang is its initial velocity. If this velocity is too fast, the matter in the universe expands too quickly and never coalesces into planets, stars, and galaxies. If the initial velocity is too slow, the universe expands only for a short time and then quickly collapses under the influence of gravity. Well-accepted cosmological models[37] tell us that the initial velocity must be specified to a precision of $1/10^{60}$. This requirement seems to overwhelm chance and has been the impetus for creative alternatives, most recently the new inflationary model of the Big Bang.

Even this newer model requires a high level of fine-tuning for it to have occurred at all and to have yielded irregularities that are neither too small nor too large for the formation of galaxies. Astrophysicists originally estimated that two components of an expansion-driving cosmological constant must cancel each other with an accuracy of better than one part in 10^{50}. In the January 1999 issue of *Scientific American*, the required accuracy was sharpened to the phenomenal exactitude of one part in 10^{123}.[38] Furthermore, the ratio of the gravitational energy to the kinetic energy must be equal to 1.00000 with a variation of less than one part in 100,000. While such estimates are being actively researched at the moment and may change over time, all possible models of the Big Bang will contain boundary conditions of a remarkably specific nature that cannot simply be described away as "fortuitous".

The Unique Design of our Habitable Planet

Astronomers F. D. Drake[39] and Carl Sagan[40] speculated during the 1960s and 1970s that Earth-like places in the universe were abundant, at least one thousand but possibly as many as one hundred million. This optimism in the ubiquity of life downplayed the specialness of planet Earth. By the 1980s, University of Virginia astronomers Trefil and Rood offered a more sober assessment in their book, *Are We Alone? The Possibility of Extraterrestrial Civilizations.*[41] They concluded that it is improbable that life exists anywhere else in the universe.

More recently, Peter Douglas Ward and Donald Brownlee of the University of Washington have taken the idea of the Earth's unique place in our vast universe to a much higher level. In their recent blockbuster book, *Rare Earth: Why Complex Life is Uncommon in the Universe*,[42] they argue that the more we learn about Earth, the more we realize how improbable is its existence as a uniquely habitable place in our universe. Ward and Brownlee state it well:

> If some god-like being could be given the opportunity to plan a sequence of events with the expressed goal of duplicating our 'Garden of Eden', that power would face a formidable task. With the best of intentions but limited by natural laws and materials it is unlikely that Earth could ever be truly replicated. Too many processes in its formation involve sheer luck. Earth-like planets could certainly be made, but each would differ in critical ways. This is well illustrated by the fantastic variety of planets and satellites (moons) that formed in our solar system. They all started with similar building materials, but the final products are vastly different from each other . . . . The physical events that led to the formation and evolution of the physical Earth required an intricate set of nearly irreproducible circumstances.[43]

What are these remarkable coincidences that have precipitated the emerging recognition of the uniqueness of Earth? Let us consider just two representative examples, *temperature control* and *plate tectonics*, both of which we have alluded to in our "needs statement" for a habitat for complex life.

Temperature Control on Planet Earth

In a universe where water is the primary medium for the chemistry of life, the temperature must be maintained between 0°C and 100°C (32°F to 212°F) for at least some portion of the year. If the temperature on earth were ever to stay below 0°C for an extended period of time, the conversion of all of Earth's water to ice would be an irreversible step.

Because ice has a very high reflectivity for sunlight, if the Earth ever becomes an ice ball, there is no returning to the higher temperatures where water exists and life can flourish. If the temperature on Earth were to exceed 100°C for an extended period of time, all oceans would evaporate, creating a vapor canopy. Again, such a step would be irreversible, since this much water in the atmosphere would efficiently trap all of the radiant heat from the sun in a "super-greenhouse effect," preventing the cooling that would be necessary to allow the steam to re-condense to water.[44] This appears to be what happened on Venus.

How does our portion of real estate in the universe remain within such a narrow temperature range, given that almost every other place in the universe is either much hotter or much colder than planet Earth, and well outside the allowable range for life?

Complex, conscious life requires an *even more narrow* temperature range of approximately 5-50°C.[45] How does our portion of real estate in the universe remain within such a narrow temperature range, given that almost every other place in the universe is either much hotter or much colder than planet Earth, and well outside the allowable range for life? First, we need to be at the right distance from the sun. In our solar system, there is a very narrow range that might permit such a temperature range to be sustained, as seen in Fig. 1. Mercury and Venus are too close to the sun, and Mars is too far away. Earth must be within approximately 10% of its actual orbit to maintain a suitable temperature range.[46]

Yet Earth's correct orbital distance from the sun is not the whole story. Our moon has an average temperature of -18°C, while Earth has an average temperature of 33°C; yet each is approximately the same average distance from the sun. Earth's atmosphere, however, efficiently traps the sun's radiant heat, maintaining the proper planetary temperature range. Humans also require an atmosphere with exactly the right proportion of tri-atomic molecules, or gases like carbon dioxide and water vapor. Small temperature variations from day to night make Earth more readily habitable. By contrast, the moon takes twenty-nine days to effectively rotate one whole period with respect to the sun, giving much larger temperature fluctuations from day to night. Earth's rotational rate is ideal to maintain our temperature within a narrow range.

Most remarkable of all, the sun's radiation has gradually increased in intensity by 40 percent over time – a fact that should have made it impossible to maintain Earth's temperature in its required range. This increase, however, has been accompanied by a gradual decrease in the Earth's concentration of carbon dioxide. Today although the Earth receives more radiation, the atmosphere traps it less efficiently, thus preserving approximately the same temperatures that the Earth experienced four billion years ago. The change in the concentration of carbon dioxide over four billion years has resulted first from plate tectonics (by which carbon dioxide has been converted to calcium carbonate in shallow waters), and more recently through the development of plant life. Such good fortune on such a grand scale must be considered a miracle in its own right. But there is still more to the story.

Mercury, Venus, and Mars all spin on their axes, but their axis angles vary chaotically from 0 to 90 degrees, giving corresponding chaotic variations in their planetary climates. Earth owes its relative climatic stability to its stable 23-degree axis of rotation. This unique stability is somehow associated with the size of Earth's large moon. Our moon is one-third the size of Earth—rare for any planet. To have such a large moon is particularly rare for planets in the inner regions of the solar system, where a habitable temperature range can be sustained. The most current theories explaining this proposition lead us again to the suspicion that such a remarkable and "fortuitous accident" occurred specifically for our benefit.[47]

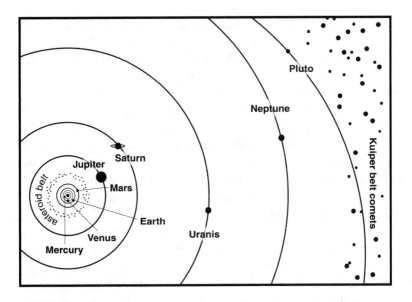

Figure 4 *In our solar system (drawn to scale), notice that the habitable zone is the region within ~10 percent of the orbital radius for planet earth, a very small part of our large, solar system.*[48]

Plate Tectonics

How does plate tectonics contribute to our planet's becoming habitable for complex life? First, plate tectonics have produced a landmass on an earth that would otherwise have remained a smooth sphere covered by 4000 feet of water. Second, plate tectonics on Earth formed regions of shallow water just beyond the landmass. In these shallows, carbon dioxide chemically reacts with calcium silicate to form calcium carbonate and silicon oxide (or sand). This process removes sufficient carbon dioxide from the atmosphere to avoid overheating as the sun's radiant energy increases. Third, plate tectonics allows for sufficiently large thermal gradients to develop the convective cells in the Earth's core that generate our magnetic field, which in turn protects us from cosmic radiation.

It is reasonable to assume that without plate tectonics, no planet could be habitable.[49] Of the 62 satellites in our solar systems, only Earth has plate tectonic activity—a fact that reflects the difficulty to meet the conditions required for this transformational process. Plate tectonics requires just the right concentration of heavy, radioactive elements in a planet or moon's core, in order to produce the proper amount of heat through radioactive decay. Furthermore, the core must be molten, with a solid, but viscous crust. The viscosity of the crust must be carefully calibrated to the heat generation in the core. The total volume of surface water present on a planet is also critical (on Earth, it is 0.5 percent by weight).[50] Too much water will yield a planet with only oceans. Too little water or too much plate tectonic activity will produce a planet with almost all land mass and very small oceans. This imbalance would leave the Earth with a water cycle that could not aerate the landmass adequately to sustain life. The oceans also buffer temperature fluctuations, helping to keep the Earth's surface temperature in a viable range. Earth's current proportion of 30 percent landmass to 70 percent oceans is biologically ideal. However, this complex end result arises from a myriad of factors that appear to be independent. Again, an explanatory model based on "accidents of nature" seems insufficient to account for yet another remarkable feature of our planet.

Design for Life: Information and The Origin of Life

We have not yet touched on the greatest "miracle" in our terrestrial narrative of origins. While we have noted the remarkable provision of a suitable universe with a local habitat that is ideal for life, the most remarkable artifact in our universe is life itself. While biological evolution, including macroevolution, continues to enjoy a larger constituency than is justified by the evidence (in my opinion), all major researchers in the field of chemical evolution (i.e., the origin of life) acknowledge the fundamental mystery of life's beginnings from inanimate matter. The enigma of the origin of life comes in the difficulty of imagining a biological system that is sufficiently complex to process energy, store information, and replicate, and yet at the same time is sufficiently simple to have just "happened" in a warm pond, as Darwin suggested, or elsewhere.

The enigma of the origin of life comes in the difficulty of imagining a biological system that is sufficiently complex to process energy, store information, and replicate, and yet at the same time is sufficiently simple to have just "happened" in a warm pond, as Darwin suggested, or elsewhere.

Complex molecules, such as proteins, RNA, and DNA, provide for essential biological functions. These biopolymers are actually long chains of simpler molecular building blocks such as amino acids (of which there are 20 different types—see *Figure 5*), sugars and bases. Their biological function is intimately connected to their precise chemical structure. How, then, were they assembled with such perfect functionality before the origin of life itself? If I stand across the street and throw paint at my curb, I am not very likely to paint "204," which is my house number. On the other hand, if I first place a template with the numbers "204" on my curb and then sling paint, I can easily paint "204" on my curb. Living systems contain their own templates. However, such templates did not guide the process before life began (i.e., under prebiotic conditions). How, then, did the templates and other molecular machinery originate?

To illustrate the staggering degree of complexity involved here, let us consider a typical protein that is composed of 100 amino acids. Amino acids are molecules that can have two mirror image structures, usually referred to as "left-handed" and "right-handed" variants, as seen in *Figure 6*. A functional protein requires the amino acids from which it is built to be (1) all left-handed; (2) all linked together with peptide bonds (*Figure 7*), and (3) all in just the right sequence to fold up into the three-dimensional structure needed for biological function, as seen in *Figure 8*. The probability of correctly assembling a functional protein in one try in a prebiotic pond, as seen in *Figure 8*, is $1/10^{190}$.[51] If we took all of the carbon in the universe, converted it into amino acids, and allowed it to chemically react at the maximum permissible rate of 10^{13} interactions per second for five billion years, the probability of making a single functioning protein increases to only $1/10^{60}$. For this reason, chance explanations for the origin of life have been rejected. Some non-random process or intelligent designer must be responsible.

However, there are no apparent nonrandom processes (such as natural selection is claimed to be in evolution) that would seem to be capable of generating the required complexity and information for the first living system.

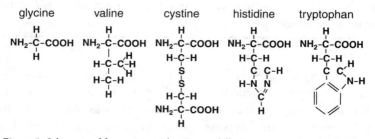

Figure 5 *Schematic of five amino acids. Twenty different amino acids are utilized in protein molecules.*

Making a viable protein from scratch is analogous to writing a sentence in a language with 20 letters in its alphabet (e.g., distinct amino acids), using a random sequencing of the letters as well as random orientations (that is upside down or sideways). Creating a coherent sentence or short paragraph from such a random sequencing of letters strains the imagination. Creating a functioning living system becomes as arduous as writing a long paragraph with such an inefficient approach. These information-generating requirements present the single, greatest obstacle to a purely naturalistic explanation for the origin of life.

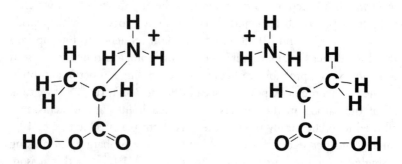

Figure 6 *Left-and right-handed versions of amino acids that occur with equal frequency in nature. Only left-handed amino acids are incorporated in protein molecules.*

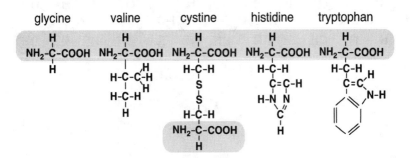

Figure 7 *Schematic representation of the formation of peptide bonds with water formed as a byproduct.*

Researchers in this field are quick to acknowledge this huge problem. For example, Miller and Levine, in their popular textbook, describe the problem as follows:

> The largest stumbling block in bridging the gap between nonliving and living still remains. All living cells are controlled by information stored in DNA, which is transcribed in RNA and them made into protein. This is a very complicated system, and each of these three molecules requires the other two—either to put it together or to help it work. DNA, for example, carries information but cannot put that information to use, or even copy itself without the help of RNA and protein.[52]

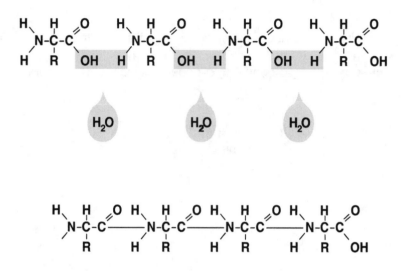

Figure 8 Schematic representation of the three-dimensional topography of a chain of amino acids. Note shape is critical to biological function.

One of the giants in origin of life research, Leslie Orgel, in a 1998 review entitled *The Origin of Life: A Review of Facts and Speculations* summarized the current state of affairs:

> There are several tenable theories about the origin of organic material on the primitive earth, but in no case is the supporting evidence compelling. Similarly, several alternative scenarios might account for the self-organization of a self-replicating entity from pre-biotic organic material, but all of those that are well formulated are based on hypothetical chemical syntheses that are problematic.[53]

Nicholas Wade noted in the *New York Times* about the origin of life:

> The chemistry of the first life is a nightmare to explain. No one has yet developed a plausible explanation to show how the earliest chemicals of life—thought to be RNA, or ribonucleic acid, a close relative of DNA, might have constructed themselves from the inorganic

chemicals likely to have been around on the early earth. The spontaneous assembly of a small RNA molecule on the primitive earth "would have been a near miracle" two experts in the subject helpfully declared last year. [54]

Interested readers are directed to my more detailed treatment of this topic in a book I co-authored entitled *The Mystery of Life's Origin: Reassessing Current Theories*[55]

Do Recent Scientific Discoveries Support Naturalism or Intelligent Design?

My initial example of design was very simple. It involved one physical law, one universal constant, and two initial conditions. These could easily be prescribed so that my water balloon would arrive on the plaza below the Leaning Tower of Pisa just in time to hit my strolling friend. This was a relatively easy design problem.

A universe that contains a special place of habitation for complex, conscious life is so remarkable that it is, realistically speaking, impossible to believe it is the result of a series of cosmic accidents. To choose to believe that there is a naturalistic explanation for (a) the mathematical forms encoded in the laws of nature, (b) the precise specification of the nineteen universal constants and (c) the remarkable initial conditions required for star formation and the simplest living systems is to believe in a miracle by another name.

A universe that contains a special place of habitation for complex, conscious life is so remarkable that it is impossible to believe it is the result of a series of cosmic accidents.

Physicist Freeman J. Dyson of Princeton's Institute for Advanced Study seems to implicitly affirm theism when he states,

> As we look out into the universe and identify the many accidents of physics and astronomy that have worked

to our benefit, it almost seems as if the universe must in some sense have known that we were coming.[56]

Physicist and Nobel laureate Arno Penzias, contemplating our enigmatic universe, observes:

> Astronomy leads us to a unique event, a universe that was created out of nothing and delicately balanced to provide exactly the conditions required to support life. In the absence of an absurdly improbable accident, the observations of modern science seem to suggest an underlying, one might say, supernatural plan.[57]

Astronomer Sir Fred Hoyle argued in *The Nature of the Universe*[58] in 1950 for the role of sheer coincidence to explain the many unique but necessary properties of the universe and of planet Earth. But the discoveries of the next thirty years dramatically changed his mind, as described in his book *The Intelligent Universe* in 1983; to quote,

> Such properties seem to run through the fabric of the natural world like a thread of happy coincidences. But there are so many odd coincidences essential to life that some explanation seems required to account for them.[59]

"But there are so many odd coincidences essential to life [in the natural world] that some explanation seems required to account for them."

Astronomer Sir Fred Hoyle

It is easy to understand why many scientists like Sir Fred Hoyle changed their minds in the past thirty years. They now agree that the universe, as we know it, cannot reasonably be explained as a cosmic accident. Frederic B. Burnham, a well-known historian of science appearing on ABC's *Nightline with Ted Koppel*, confirmed the current openness to the intelligent design model with his comment,

The scientific community is prepared to consider the idea that God created the universe a more respectable hypothesis today than at any time in the last 100 years.[60]

Conclusion

Returning to the Mt. Rushmore illustration with which we began, we must ask ourselves whether our universe and place in it (planet Earth) are more analogous to Mt. Rushmore or to the rock in Hawaii that captures John F. Kennedy's silhouette in its shadow? It seems to me the answer is perfectly clear, based on the myriad of information presented in this paper and the much larger amount of related information in the literature, that the universe is better represented in its complexity by Mt. Rushmore. However, Mt. Rushmore is an inadequate analogy to our universe and habitat in it.

If a few portions of the Mt. Rushmore monument had been made incorrectly, the impressions of the four presidents would not be completely lost, just less accurate. But, if any one of the five fundamental laws of nature is lacking, if any of the universal constants is outside the permissible range of values, or if any of the many initial conditions is not met, then any potential for life in our universe would be obliterated.

I must conclude that it takes a great deal more faith to believe in an accidental universe than to believe in an intelligent creator, or God ....

The design requirements for our universe are like a chain of 1000 links. *If any link breaks, we do not have a less optimal universe for life. We have a universe incapable of sustaining life!* The evidence I presented is daunting, but still short of "proof." I must conclude that it takes a great deal more faith to believe in an accidental universe than to believe in an intelligent creator, or God, who crafted such a marvelous universe and beautiful place of habitation in planet Earth, and then created life (including human beings) to occupy it.

Audience Discussion[61]

Q1: I have a question regarding an infinitely bouncing universe. I think that if there is enough mass in the universe as it expands, it will eventually decelerate, stop, and collapse. My question is this: As it collapses couldn't it bounce, and simply expand and contract infinitely? If so, if every time it comes out with a different set of constants, sooner or later you are going to get it right.

This is an interesting possibility that was suggested by several scientists in the 1970s to avoid the theistic implications of the Big Bang. In 1983 Alan Guth, who also developed the inflationary theory as a component of Big Bang cosmology, published his analysis of the possibility of an infinitely bouncing universe in *Nature*,[62] addressing this very question. Guth and Sher concluded that if the universe is closed, it will not bounce, it would simply go "thud." Bludman[63] came to exactly the same conclusion. To avoid the results of these analyses, Hawking in his book *A Brief History of Time* posited that the second law of thermodynamics might be reversed in a collapsing universe, a rather silly idea that Hawking has now supposedly retracted.

The argument goes like this. If you drop a superball, one whose collision with the floor is almost perfectly elastic with no energy dissipation, then it will bounce back to the original release height. If you drop a piece of clay, it simply sticks to the floor, dissipating all of the kinetic energy on impact, with no residual bounce. Is an explosion such as the big bang energy-conserving or energy-dissipating? Explosions are, of course, very energy dissipative, rendering an infinitely bouncing universe impossible.

Q2: What is the possibility of an infinite number of alternative universes?

The question is an excellent one and implies that you fully appreciate the dilemma that modern science has created through its determination that we live in a remarkable place in a remarkable universe that seems impossible to imagine "just happening by a remarkable accident in a single try." First, let me agree that it is not logically impossible to imagine multiple universes, maybe even an indefinite number of alternative universes. But it is scientifically impossible to determine the existence, much less the nature, of such universes if they exist. It is physically impossible to "see" outside our universe. Thus, the hypothesis of an infinite number of alternative universes will always be a metaphysical assumption not different in kind from the metaphysical assumption of an Intelligent Designer and Creator. One must choose between these assumptions based on what one believes to be most reasonable. However, other kinds of evidence than scientific evidence may be helpful in making this choice. For example, is there historical evidence for an Intelligent Creator, evidence that this Creator intervened in history one or multiple times subsequent to his creation? Is there existential evidence from people's personal experience that might suggest the existence of God? Taken as a whole, I think it takes much less faith to believe in a universe created by an Intelligent Designer than to believe in an infinite number of alternative universes.

Q3: What are your thoughts on an interventionist God vs. simply an Intelligent Designer?

An Intelligent Designer could have made a universe that unfolds seamlessly or unfolds with some discontinuities. Some Christian scientists like Howard Van Til have a strong preference for a creation that has all of the design put in "at the front end." If I can relate this to mathematics, a seamless unfolding assumes that only initial boundary conditions are important, with no additional information brought to bear on the system over time. This seems to be at odds with what we have actually found.

Some Christians are uncomfortable with an interventionist God as they fear a "God of the gaps" mentality that can leave us with a God who shrinks as we find more so-called natural explanations of how things happen. However, in my presentations and writings I have only posited God's supernatural intervention in *his order* where what is needed is additional information. Natural laws are sufficient to provide us with the formal conditions for order (as in crystals) or chaos (as in weather), but are *insufficient* for specified complexities such as we have in DNA encoding or in the specification of the universal constants.

I believe as a matter of simplicity and economy that God added information at certain critical points in the history of the universe rather than creating an unnecessarily complex universe where all the information could be incorporated at the beginning. The question of which explanation is more reasonable is a scientific question as well as a theological question. The Genesis account, if taken as real history rather than pure poetry, would seem to support a God who intervenes, at least occasionally, as his creation story unfolds. This is not conceptually problematic.

Q4: A fellow from Australia named Satterwhite has claimed that the speed of light is not constant after all, but is slowing down over time. Do you believe this is so, and if you do, how would it affect your argument about the universal constants?

What Satterwhite has done is to take all of the recorded measurements of the speed at which light travels that have been made in history and plotted them on a graph. The graph seems to indicate the speed of light is decreasing with the passage of time. However, if you plot the error bars on his measurements rather than using just the averages, you discover that there is a change in the error bar size due to a natural bias in the measurements that always gives a high indication of the speed of light. As measurements became more precise, the error bars shrank in size, giving an erroneous impression of a decrease in the speed of light rather than what was actually the case, namely a decrease in the error bar size. I don't believe any physicist today believes that the speed of light or any other universal constant changes, and there is no empirical evidence to support such a claim. If such changes did indeed occur, they would have to change in a highly coordinated way to maintain a universe suitable to support complex, conscious life.

Q5: The constants we have at this point in time don't appear to be causally connected in the assignment of values. If a Grand Unified Theory is discovered, the number of independent constants would be reduced in part. I wonder if there is an alternative universe, why the speed of light is $3x10^8$, and whether we are just lucky it happened to be that value. Why is it that the gravity force constant is 1036 times *weaker than the electromagnetic constant? If this is the only universe we know, we can easily hypothesize alternative possibilities and we discover quickly that almost all the alternatives are not possible. They don't create a universe in which we could exist so we are left with the only universe we know and it is highly tuned to produce a very ideal habitat for life. Why?*

That the universal constants are exactly what they need to be to provide a universe where life can exist is an enigma. How they got that way brings us to the possibility of an Intelligent Designer and I think this is the most reasonable explanation. Why this Creator wanted to make such a place for life and then life itself is a theological, rather than scientific, question. If the Grand Unified Theory is ever successfully completed, it will surely reduce the number of independent constants (i.e., some are dependent on others in a lawful way), but, at the same time, will make the allowable range even tighter than it is for the larger number of apparently independent constants we discussed here.

Q6: Do you believe that there is life in other parts of the universe, either because it forms easily or is inevitable–as Carl Sagan claimed— or because an Intelligent Creator just chose to make life in multiple locations and/or at multiple times?

It is an interesting question for which I have no informed opinion. My hunch is that there is not life in other parts of the universe, but I see no reason why the Intelligent Creator might not have chosen to create it in other parts of the universe as well. Carl Sagan's belief that life is easily formed and is abundant in the universe, which is the basis for the search for extraterrestrial intelligence (SETI), has never been supported by scientific evidence for the origin of life. Thus, if an Intelligent Creator didn't create it at multiple locations, it likely exists only on planet Earth.

Q7: The probability of a certain set of people being at the train station on a certain day at a certain time, and the probability of getting a certain bridge hand, is extremely small, but they happen every day. Why can't we explain our highly improbable universe in the same way?

Your question is very insightful, but there is a good explanation. Let's suppose that a certain bridge hand—all spades, all hearts, all clubs and all diamonds—corresponds to a universe just like ours, with everything just so. Let's assume all other hands correspond to a universe that is dysfunctional in some way, what I will call wrong hands. Now the probability of any one wrong hand is extremely small, but there are so many different wrong hands that the probability of getting of such a hand is essentially one (i.e., probabilistically assured). So though there are many ways to be unsuccessful in my bridge hand, there is just one way to be successful. Thus, being successful is extremely improbable while being unsuccessful is almost certain. If I wanted to predict ahead of time a certain group of people at the train station at a certain time, this would be extremely difficult, and my chance of success would be small. However, my chance of being unsuccessful would be essentially one, as there are many combinations of people that differ from my prediction, each individually improbable but taken together give a high probability of an unsuccessful prediction of who would be there. So it is with our universe.

Allow me to recommend a fine book that addresses this problem of improbabilities and design inference. The book is by Dr. William A. Dembski and is titled, *The Design Inference*.[64]

Q8: But given so much time, isn't anything possible?

With regard to the origin of life, a very improbable event by everyone's estimation, Dr. George Wald, Nobel laureate in chemistry, said in 1958 that time is the hero of this story implying that given enough time even the improbable becomes probable. But Wald spoke at a time when many scientists thought that the universe was infinitely old and that therefore we had an infinity of time. Today with the widespread acceptance of Big Bang cosmology, it is clear that the time period that the universe existed is quite finite, and the time for the origin of life is at most a few hundred, million years, which is too small to make an accidental origin of life believable.

Dean Kenyon and George Steinman in their book, *Biochemical Predestination*[65] did a calculation in which they assumed all the carbon in the universe was on the surface of the earth in the form of amino acids. They further assumed that these amino acids reacted at the maximum possible rate of 10^{13} times per second. They then assumed these circumstances persisted for one billion years to see what they might make in accidental reactions. They concluded that they might make one half of one functional protein molecule. They dismissed chance as the explanation for the origin of life. Chance is nothing more than the god of the gaps of the atheist.

Q9: *Why do we need a universe like this one? If the universe were different, we would be different in some appropriate way, wouldn't we?*

I agree and indicated so in my talk. Our universe is not the only possible one where life might exist, but there are some design features that must be satisfied by any universe where life can exist, as also noted in my talk. For example, there would need to be sufficient elemental diversity, long-term sources of energy, and a matching of the energy (from the sun in our case) to the bonding energy of the various elements. Almost all combinations of universal constants produce a universe with at most one element (or none) and no sun. Thus, what is remarkable is not that we have exactly the universe we have, but that we have a universe that is suitable to support life at all.

Q10: *Why accept the God of the Bible? I don't see how you get that out of the scientific evidence that you presented tonight.*

You are quite correct. The evidence presented points to the existence of an intelligent creator, but not uniquely to the God of the Bible. I have looked primarily at the scientific evidence. The Apostle Paul said in Romans 1 that God's revelation (our knowledge of him) is accessible in the evidence of nature: "Ever since the creation of the world, God's invisible attributes—His eternal power and divine nature—have been clearly seen, being understood through what has been made." (Romans

1:20a). The Apostle Paul meant something quite different than what I have discussed because Paul understood much less about nature at that time than we understand today. I believe that implies that God has not left us to make a blind leap of faith. Some people believe that faith is something you either have (like the talent to play the piano) or you don't have (like playing basketball in my case).

God purposefully gave us strong evidence to "know He exists" from what we see in creation. Therefore, we shouldn't go on ignoring the implications of this evidence and what it means. This Creator has a purpose for our lives and has revealed Himself to us so we might have a relationship with Him. This furnishes the context for making sense of the Bible's miraculous claims and its testimony to God's deeply personal involvement in history in the person of Jesus Christ.

If there is evidence for God's existence, then it is reasonable that God might persuade us that this Jesus Christ person was God incarnate. Believing in a resurrection from the dead is difficult if I have no independent evidence for God's existence. But if I have considerable evidence for God's existence, then it is certainly within reason that God might bring Jesus back from the dead, thus vindicating his claims. Believing in Jesus' Resurrection for me is made much easier by the remarkable phenomena I see in our magnificent universe. As a painting in an art gallery suggests a painter, our universe points to a creator who has left his signature everywhere. That is a very compelling existential argument for God's existence.

---

[1] Paley, William. *Natural Theology* (London: Wilks and Taylor, 1802).

[2] Dawkins, Richard. *Climbing Mount Improbable* (New York: Norton, 1996): 3.

[3] Ibid.

[4] Ibid.

[5] Kepler, Johannes. *Defundamentis Astrologiae Certioribus*, Thesis XX (1601).

[6] Galilei, Galileo; this comment is widely attributed to Galileo, but without reference.

[7] Kline, Morris. *Mathematics: The Loss of Certainty* (New York: Oxford University Press, 1980): 52.

[8] Ibid.

[9] Wigner, Eugene. "The Unreasonable Effectiveness of Mathematics in the Physical Sciences," *Communications on Pure and Applied Mathematics* 13 (1960): 1-14.

[10] Einstein, Albert. *Letters to Solovine* (New York: Philosophical Library, 1987): 131.

[11] Courant, Richard, *Partial Differential Equations*, Vol. II of R. Courant and D. Hilbert, *Methods of Mathematical Physics* (New York: Interscience Publishers, 1962): 765–66.

[12] Davies, Paul. *Superforce* (New York: Simon and Schuster, 1984): 243.

[13] Hoyle, Fred. *Religion and the Scientists*, quoted in John Barrow and Frank Tipler, *The Anthropic Cosmological Principle* (Oxford: Clarendon Press, 1988): 22.

[14] Barrow, John and Frank Tipler. *The Anthropic Cosmological Principle* (Oxford: Clarendon Press, 1988).

[15] Leslie, John. *Universes* (New York: Routledge, 1989).

[16] Davies, Paul. *The Accidental Universe* (Cambridge: Cambridge University Press, 1982).

[17] Davies, Paul. *Superforce* (Portsmouth, N.H.: Heinemann, 1984).

[18] Davies, Paul. *The Cosmic Blueprint* (Portsmouth, N.H.: Heinemann, 1988).

[19] Gribbin, John and Martin Rees. *Cosmic Coincidences* (New York: Bantam Books, 1989).

[20] Breuer, Reinhard. *The Anthropic Principle*, trans. Harry Newman and Mark Lowery (Boston: Birkhäuser, 1991).

[21] Cohen-Tannoudji, Gilles. *Universal Constants in Physics,* trans. Patricia Thickstun (New York: McGraw-Hill, 1993).

[22] Moreland, J. P. ed., *The Creation Hypothesis* (Downers Grove, IL: InterVarsity Press, 1994).

[23] Dembski, William A. ed., *Mere Creation: Science, Faith & Intelligent Design.* (Downers Grove, IL: InterVarsity Press, 1998).

[24] Leslie, John. *Universes* (New York: Routledge,1989): 36-39.

[25] Barrow and Tipler. *The Anthropic Cosmological Principle*, 336.

[26] Michael J. Denton, *Nature's Destiny: How the Laws of Biology Reveal Purpose in the Universe* (New York: Simon and Schuster, 1998): 56-57.

[27] *Encyclopedia Britannica* (1994), 15th ed., Vol. 18, 200.

[28] Barrow and Tipler, *Anthropic Cosmological Principle*, 322.

[29] Rozental, I.L., *On Numerical Values of Fundamental Constants* (Moscow: 1980): 9.

[30] Leslie, John. *Universes*, 35-40.

[31] Hoyle, F., D.N.F. Dunbar, W.A. Wensel, and W. Whaling, *Phys. Rev.* 92 (1953): 649.

[32] Hoyle, F., *Annual Review of Astronomy and Astrophysics* 20 (1982): 16.

[33] Hawking, Stephen, *Physics Bulletin: Cambridge* 32 (1980): 15.

[34] Barrow and Tipler, *The Anthropic Cosmological Principle*, 371.

[35] Breuer, Reinhard. *The Anthropic Principle: Man as the Focal Point of Nature* (Boston: Birkhauser, 1990): 102.

[36] Wheeler, John. *Reader's Digest*, September 1986, 107.

[37] Davies, Paul. *The Accidental Universe* (Cambridge: Cambridge University Press, 1982): 90.

[38] Krauss, Lawrence M., "Cosmological Antigravity," *Scientific American* 280 (January 1999): 53-59.

[39] Drake, F. D. and Dava Sobel, *Is Anyone Out There?* (New York: Delacorte Press, 1992): 62.

40 Shklovskii, I. S. and C. Sagan, *Intelligent Life in the Universe* (New York: Dell, 1966).

41 Rood, Robert and James S. Trefil, *Are We Alone? The Possibility of Extraterrestrial Civilizations* (New York: Scribner, 1981).

42 Ward, Peter B. and Donald Brownlee, *Rare Earth: Why Complex Life is Uncommon in the Universe* (New York: Copernicus, 2000).

43 Ibid., 37.

44 Broecker, W., *How to Build a Habitable Planet* (Palisades, NY: Eldigio Press, 1985): 197-229.

45 Ward and Brownlee, *Rare Earth*, 19-20.

46 Ibid., 15-33.

47 J.Kasting, J.,"Habitable Zones Around Stars: An Update," in *Circumstellar Habitable Zones*, ed. L. Doyle (Menlo Park, CA: Travis House, 1996): 17-28.

48 Ward and Brownlee, *Rare Earth*, 15-33.

49 Ibid., 208.

50 Ibid., 264-265.

51 Miller, Kenneth R. and Joseph Levine, *Biology: The Living Science* (Upper Saddle River, NJ: Prentice Hall, 1998): 406-407.

52 Bradley, Walter L. and Charles B. Thaxton, "Information and the Origin of Life", in *The Creation Hypothesis: Scientific Evidence for an Intelligent Designer*, ed. J.P. Moreland (Downers Grove, IL: InterVarsity Press, 1994): 190.

53 Miller, Kenneth R. and Joseph Levine, *Biology: The Living Science* (Upper Saddle River, NJ: Prentice Hall, 1998): 406-407.

54 Nicholas Wade. "Genetic Analysis Yields Intimations of a Primordial Commune", *New York Times*, 14 June 2000, from website.

55 Thaxton, Charles B. ,Walter L. Bradley, and Roger L. Olsen. *Mystery of Life's Origin: Reassessing Current Theories* (New York: Philosophical Library, 1984).

56 Dyson, Freeman J., cited in Barrow and Tipler, *Anthropic Cosmological Principle*, 318.

57 Penzias, Arno , *Our Universe: Accident or Design* (Wits, S. Africa: Starwatch, 1992): 42.

58 Hoyle, Fred, *The Nature of the Universe* (New York: Harper, 1950): 101.

59 Hoyle, Fred, *The Intelligent Universe* (London: Michael Joseph, 1983): 220.

60 ABC's *Nightline with Ted Koppel*, 24 April 1992.

61 This audience discussion followed a lecture by the author when he spoke on, "Is There Scientific Evidence for the Existence of God?" a recent Veritas Forum at Princeton University, but this audience discussion is typical of the responses Dr. Bradley receives around the country.

62 Guth, Alan H. and Marc Sher, "The Impossibility of a Bouncing Universe", *Nature* 302 (1983): 505.

63 Bludman, S.A., "Thermodynamics and the end of a closed Universe", *Nature* 308 (1984): 319.

64 Dembski, William A., *The Design Inference*. (Cambridge: Cambridge University Press, 1998).

65 Kenyon, Dean and George Steinman, *Biochemical Predestination* (New York: McGraw Hill, 1969).

Chapter Seven

◆〜◆〜◆

THE MODERN INTELLIGENT
DESIGN HYPOTHESIS:
BREAKING THE RULES[1]

Michael J. Behe

Dr. Michael J. Behe is Professor of Biological Sciences at Lehigh University. He received his Ph.D. in Biochemistry from the University of Pennsylvania in 1978. Behe's current research involves delineation of design and natural selection in protein structures. In addition to publishing over 35 articles in refereed biochemical journals, he has also written editorial features in Boston Review, The American Spectator, and The New York Times. His book, Darwin's Black Box, discusses the implications for neo-Darwinism of what he calls "irreducibly complex" biochemical systems.

Abstract

The modern hypothesis of intelligent design of molecular aspects of life is contrasted with older versions of the design hypothesis, exemplified by the writings of William Paley. The modern hypothesis is at once more restricted than older versions—limiting itself to a conclusion of design rather than going on to claim the designer is God—and more powerful, since it is not vulnerable to the argument from evil or other arguments that presume the designer is God. I also examine several counter-examples that have been advocated by scientific opponents of design and show them to be inadequate.

IN THIS ESSAY, I ARGUE THAT SOME BIOLOGICAL systems at the molecular level appear to be the result of deliberate intelligent design (ID). I am well aware that arguments for design in biology have been made before, most notably by William Paley in the 19th century. But, it is important to clearly distinguish modern arguments for intelligent design from earlier versions.

Differences from Paley

The most important difference is that my argument is limited to design itself; I strongly emphasize that it is not an argument for the existence of a benevolent God, as Paley's was. I, myself, believe in a benevolent God, but while I recognize that philosophy and theology may be able to extend the argument, a scientific argument for design in biology is not. Thus, while I argue for design, the question of the identity of the designer is open. Of course, some possibilities for the role of designer may seem more plausible than others based on information from fields other than science. Nonetheless, in regard to the identity of the designer, modern ID theory happily echoes Isaac Newton's phrase, hypothesis non fingo, meaning "I make no hypothesis."

The fact that modern intelligent design theory is a minimalist argument for design itself, not an argument for the existence of God, relieves it of much baggage that weighed down Paley's argument. *First*, it is immune to the argument from evil. It does not matter to the scientific case whether the designer is good or bad, interested in us or disinterested. It only matters that an explanation of design appears to be consistent with the biological examples to which I point. *Second*, questions about whether the designer is omnipotent do not arise in my case, as they did in Paley's. Perhaps the designer isn't omnipotent or very competent. More to the point, perhaps the designer was not interested in every detail of biology, as Paley thought, so that while some features were indeed designed, others were left to the vagaries of nature. Thus, the modern argument for design need only show that intelligent agency appears to be a good explanation for some biological features.

Compared to William Paley's argument, modern ID theory is very restricted in scope. However, what it lacks in scope, it makes up for in resilience. Paley conjoined a number of separable ideas in his argument—design, omnipotence, benevolence, and so on—which made his overall position quite brittle. For example, arguments against the perceived benevolence of the design became arguments against the very existence of design. Thus, one got the seeming non sequitur stating that because biological feature A appears malevolent, therefore all biological features arose by natural selection or some other unintelligent process. With the much more modest claims of modern ID theory, such a move is not possible. Attention is focused on the basic question of whether unintelligent processes could produce the complex structures of biology, or whether intelligence was indeed required.

Therefore, mine is a *scientific* argument, not a philosophical or theological one. Let me explain what I mean without getting entangled in trying to define those elusive terms. By calling the argument scientific, I mean, first, that it does not rest on any tenet of any particular creed, nor is it a deductive argument from first principles. Rather, it depends critically on physical evidence found in nature. Second, because it depends on physical evidence it can potentially be falsified by other physical evidence. Thus, it only claims to currently be the best explanation, given the information we have available right now.

I acknowledge that the scientific argument for design may have theological implications, but that does not change its status as a scientific idea. I would like to draw a parallel between the modern argument for design in biology and the Big Bang theory in physics. The Big Bang theory strikes many people as having theological implications, as shown by those who do not welcome those implications. For example in 1989, John Maddox, the editor of *Nature*, the world's leading science journal, published a very peculiar editorial, entitled "Down with the Big Bang." He wrote:

> Apart from being philosophically unacceptable, the Big Bang is an over-simple view of how the Universe began, and it is unlikely to survive the decade ahead....

Creationists ... seeking support for their opinions have ample justification in the Big Bang.[2]

I will now consider the scientific case for intelligent design in biology. First, I make the case for design. Second, I will address several specific scientific objections put forward by critics of design. Finally, I will discuss the question of falsifiability.

Darwinism and Design

In 1859, Charles Darwin published his great work *On the Origin of Species*[3], in which he proposed to explain how the great variety and complexity of the natural world might have been produced solely by the action of blind physical processes. His proposed mechanism was natural selection working on random variation. In a nutshell, Darwin reasoned that the members of a species whose chance variation gave them an edge in the struggle to survive would tend to survive and reproduce. If the variation could be inherited, then over time the characteristics of the species would change. Over great periods of time, perhaps great changes would occur.

If it could be demonstrated that any complex organ existed which could not possibly have been formed by numerous, successive, slight modifications, my theory would absolutely break down.

Charles Darwin, *Origin of the Species (1859)*

It was a very elegant idea. Nonetheless, Darwin knew his proposed mechanism could not explain everything and in the *Origin* he gave us a criterion by which to judge his theory. He wrote:

> If it could be demonstrated that any complex organ existed which could not possibly have been formed by numerous, successive, slight modifications, my theory would absolutely break down.[4]

He added, however, that he could "find out no such case." Of course, Darwin was justifiably interested in protecting his fledgling theory from easy dismissal, and so he put the burden of proof on opponents to prove a negative—to "demonstrate" that something "could not possibly" have happened. This is essentially impossible to do in science. Nonetheless, let's ask what might at least *potentially* meet Darwin's criterion? What sort of organ or system seems unlikely to be formed by "numerous, successive, slight modifications"? A good place to start is with one that is *irreducibly complex*. In *Darwin's Black Box: The Biochemical Challenge to Evolution*, I defined an irreducibly complex system as:

> a single system which is composed of several well-matched, interacting parts that contribute to the basic function, and where the removal of any one of the parts causes the system to effectively cease functioning.[5]

A good illustration of an irreducibly complex system from our everyday world is a simple mechanical mousetrap. A common mousetrap has several parts, including a wooden platform, a spring with extended ends, a hammer, holding bar, and catch. Now, if the mousetrap is missing the spring, or hammer, or platform, it doesn't catch mice half as well as it used to, or a quarter as well. It simply doesn't catch mice at all. Therefore, it is irreducibly complex. It turns out that irreducibly complex systems are headaches for Darwinian theory, because they are resistant to being produced in the gradual, step-by-step manner that Darwin envisioned.

As biology has progressed with dazzling speed in the past half century, we have discovered many systems in the cell, at the very foundation of life, which, like a mousetrap, are irreducibly complex. Space permits me to mention only one example here—the bacterial flagellum. The flagellum is quite literally an outboard motor that some bacteria use to swim. It is a rotary device that, like a motorboat, turns a propeller to push against liquid, moving the bacterium forward in the process. It consists of a number of parts, including a long tail that acts as a propeller, the hook region which attaches the propeller to the drive shaft, the motor which uses a flow of acid from the outside of the bacterium to the inside to power the turning, a stator which keeps the structure stationary in the plane of the membrane while the propeller turns, and bushing material to allow the drive shaft to poke up through the bacterial membrane. In the absence of the hook, or the motor, or the propeller, or the drive shaft, or most of the 40 different types of proteins that genetic studies have shown to be necessary for the activity or construction of the flagellum, one doesn't get a flagellum that spins half as fast as it used to, or a quarter as fast. Either the flagellum doesn't work, or it doesn't even get constructed in the cell. Like a mousetrap, the flagellum is irreducibly complex. And again like the mousetrap, its evolutionary development by "numerous, successive, slight modifications" is quite difficult to envision. In fact, if one examines the scientific literature, one quickly sees that no one has ever proposed a serious, detailed model for how the flagellum might have arisen in a Darwinian manner, let alone conducted experiments to test such a model. Thus, in a flagellum we seem to have a serious candidate to meet Darwin's criterion by which to judge his theory. We have a system that seems very unlikely to have been produced by "numerous, successive, slight modifications."

Is there an alternative explanation for the origin of the flagellum? I think there is, and it's really pretty easy to see. But in order to see it, we have to do something a bit unusual: we have to break a rule. The rule is rarely stated explicitly, but it was stated candidly by Nobel laureate Christian De Duve in his 1995 book, *Vital Dust*, in which he speculated on the expansive history of life. He wrote:

> A warning: All through this book, I have tried to conform to the overriding rule that life be treated as a natural process, its origin, evolution, and manifestations, up to and including the human species, as governed by the same laws as nonliving processes.[6]

In science journals the rule is always obeyed in letter, yet sometimes it is violated in spirit. For example, several years ago David DeRosier, professor of biology at Brandeis University, published a review article on the bacterial flagellum in which he remarked:

"More so than other motors, the flagellum resembles a machine designed by a human."[7]

That same year, the journal *Cell*[8] published a special issue on the topic of "Macromolecular Machines." On the cover of the journal was a painting of a stylized protein apparently in the shape of an animal, with what seems to be a watch in the foreground (perhaps William Paley's watch). Articles in the journal had titles such as, "The Cell as a Collection of Protein Machines;" "Polymerases and the Replisome: Machines within Machines;" and "Mechanical Devices of the Spliceosome: Motors, Clocks, Springs, and Things." By way of introduction, on the contents page was written:

> Like the machines invented by humans to deal efficiently with the macroscopic world, protein assemblies contain highly coordinated moving parts.[9]

If the flagellum and other biochemical systems strike scientists as looking like "machines" that were "designed by a human" or "invented by humans," why don't we entertain the idea that perhaps they were indeed designed by an intelligent being? We don't do that, of course, because it would violate the rule.

Some of my critics say that intelligent design is a religious idea, not a scientific one. I disagree. Intelligent design is completely empirical. It is based entirely on the physical evidence.

Sometimes, when a fellow is feeling frisky, he throws caution to the wind and breaks a few rules. In fact, that is what I did in Darwin's Black Box: I proposed that, rather than Darwinian evolution, a more compelling explanation for the irreducibly complex molecular machines discovered in the cell is that they were indeed designed, as David De Rosier and the editors of *Cell* apprehended — purposely designed by an intelligent agent. That proposal has attracted a bit of attention. Some of my critics asserted that the proposal of intelligent design is a religious idea, not a scientific one. I disagree. The conclusion of intelligent design in these cases is completely empirical. It is based entirely on the physical evidence, along with an appreciation for how we come to a conclusion of design.

Every day of our lives we decide, consciously or not, that some things were designed and others were not. How do we come to a conclusion of design?

To help see how we conclude design, imagine you are walking with a friend in the woods. Suddenly your friend is pulled up by the ankle by a vine and left dangling in the air. After you cut him down you reconstruct the situation. You see that the vine was tied to a tree limb that was bent down and held by a stake in the ground. Leaves covered the vine so you wouldn't notice it, and so on. From the way the parts were arranged, you would quickly conclude that this was no accident— this was a designed trap. That is not a religious conclusion, but one based firmly in the physical evidence.

Although I think intelligent design is a rather obvious hypothesis, my book seems to have caught a number of people by surprise. It has been reviewed widely by the *New York Times*, the *Washington Post*, and other major media. Unexpectedly, not everyone agreed with me. In response to my argument, several scientists pointed to experimental results which, they claim, either cast much doubt over the claim of intelligent design, or outright falsify it.

In the remainder of this essay, I will discuss these counterexamples and show why I think they not only fail to support Darwinism, but why they actually fit much better with a theory of intelligent design. After that, I will discuss the issue of falsifiability.

An "Evolved" Operon

Kenneth Miller, a professor of cell biology at Brown University, has written a book recently, entitled *Finding Darwin's God*[10], in which he defends Darwinism from a variety of critics, including myself. In a chapter devoted to rebutting *Darwin's Black Box*, he correctly states that "a true acid test" of the ability of Darwinism to deal with irreducible complexity would be to "[use] the tools of molecular genetics to wipe out an existing multipart system and then see if evolution can come to the rescue with a system to replace it."[11] He then cites the careful work over the past 25 years of Barry Hall[12] of the University of Rochester on the experimental evolution of a lactose-utilizing system in *E. coli*.

Here is a brief description of how the system, called the *lac* operon, functions. The lac operon of *E. coli* contains genes coding for several proteins that are involved in the metabolism of a type of sugar called lactose. One protein of the *lac* operon, called a permease, imports lactose through the otherwise-impermeable cell membrane. Another protein is an enzyme called galactosidase, which can break down lactose to its two constituent monosaccharides, galactose and glucose, which the cell can then process further. Because lactose is rarely available in the environment, the bacterial cell switches off the genes until lactose is available. The switch is controlled by another protein called a repressor, whose gene is located next to the operon. Ordinarily the repressor binds to the *lac* operon, shutting it off by physically interfering with the operon. However, in the presence of the natural "inducer" allolactose or the artificial chemical inducer IPTG, the repressor binds to the inducer and releases the operon, allowing the *lac* operon enzymes to be synthesized by the cell.

After giving his interpretation of Barry Hall's experiments, Kenneth Miller excitedly remarks:

> Think for a moment—if we were to happen upon the interlocking biochemical complexity of the reevolved lactose system, wouldn't we be impressed by the intelligence of its design? Lactose triggers a regulatory sequence that switches on the synthesis of an enzyme that then metabolizes lactose itself. The products of that successful lactose metabolism then activate the gene for the lac permease, which ensures a steady supply of lactose entering the cell. Irreducible complexity. What good would the permease be without the galactosidase? ... No good, of course.
>
> By the very same logic applied by Michael Behe to other systems, therefore, we could conclude that the system had been designed. Except we *know* that it was *not* designed. We know it evolved because we watched

it happen right in the laboratory! No doubt about it—the evolution of biochemical systems, even complex multipart ones, is explicable in terms of evolution. Behe is wrong.[13]

I will try to show that the picture Miller paints is greatly exaggerated. In fact, far from being a difficulty for design, the very same work that Miller points to as an example of Darwinian prowess, I would cite as showing the limits of Darwinism and the need for design.

In fact, far from being a difficulty for design, the very same work that Miller points to as an example of Darwinian prowess, I would cite as showing the limits of Darwinism and the need for design.

So what did Barry Hall actually do? To study bacterial evolution in the laboratory, in the mid 1970's Hall produced a strain of *E. coli* in which the gene for just the galactosidase of the *lac* operon was deleted. He later wrote:

> All of the other functions for lactose metabolism, including lactose permease and the pathways for metabolism of glucose and galactose, the products of lactose hydrolysis, remain intact, thus re-acquisition of lactose utilization requires only the evolution of a new b-galactosidase function.[14]

Thus, contrary to Miller's own criterion for "a true acid test," a multipart system was not "wiped out"—only one component of a multipart system was deleted. The lac permease and repressor remained intact. Moreover, as we shall see, the artificial inducer IPTG was added to the bacterial culture, and an alternate, cryptic galactosidase was left intact.

Without galactosidase, Hall's cells could not grow when cultured on a medium containing only lactose as a food source. However, when grown on a plate that also included alternative nutrients, bacterial colonies could be established. When the other nutrients were exhausted the colonies stopped growing. However, Hall noticed that after several days to several weeks, hyphae grew on some of the colonies. By isolating cells from the hyphae, Hall saw they frequently had two mutations, one of which was in a gene for a protein he called "evolved b-galactosidase," ("*ebg*") which allowed it to metabolize lactose efficiently. The *ebg* gene is located in another operon, distant from the *lac* operon, and is under the control of its own repressor protein. The second mutation Hall found was always in the gene for the *ebg* repressor protein, which caused the repressor to bind lactose with sufficient strength to de-repress the *ebg* operon.

The fact that there were two separate mutations in different genes—neither of which by itself allowed cell growth[15]—startled Hall, who knew that the odds against the mutations appearing randomly and independently were prohibitive.[16] Hall's results and similar results from other laboratories led to research in a new area dubbed "adaptive mutations." (Cairns[17]; Foster[18]; Hall[19]; McFadden and Al Khalili[20]; Shapiro[21]). As Hall later wrote:

> Adaptive mutations are mutations that occur in non-dividing or slowly dividing cells during prolonged nonlethal selection, and that appear to be specific to the challenge of the selection in the sense that the only mutations that arise are those that provide a growth advantage to the cell. The issue of the specificity has been controversial because it violates our most basic assumptions about the randomness of mutations with respect to their effect on the cell.[22]

The mechanism(s) of adaptive mutation are currently unknown. While they are being sorted out, it seems unwise to cite results of processes which "violate our most basic assumptions about the randomness of mutations" to argue for Darwinian evolution, as Miller does.

The nature of adaptive mutation aside, a strong reason to consider Barry Hall's results to be quite modest is that the *ebg* proteins—both the repressor and galactosidase—are homologous to the *E. coli lac* proteins and overlap the proteins in activity. Both of the unmutated *ebg* proteins already bind lactose. Binding of lactose even to the unmutated *ebg* repressor induces a 100-fold increase in synthesis of the *ebg* operon.[23] Even the unmutated *ebg* galactosidase can hydrolyze lactose at a level of about 10% that of a "Class II" mutant galactosidase that supports cell growth.[24] These activities are not sufficient to permit growth of *E. coli* on lactose, but they already are present. The mutations reported by Hall simply enhance pre-existing activities of the proteins. In a recent paper [25], Professor Hall pointed out that both the lac and *ebg* galactosidase enzymes are part of a family of highly-conserved galactosidases, identical at 13 of 15 active site amino acid residues, which apparently diverged by gene duplication more than two billion years ago. The two mutations in *ebg* galactosidase that increase its ability to hydrolyze lactose change two nonidentical residues back to those of other galactosidases, so that their active sites are identical. Thus—before any experiments were done—the *ebg* active site was already a near-duplicate of other galactosidases, and only became more active by becoming a complete duplicate. By phylogenetic analysis, Hall concluded that those two mutations are the *only* ones in *E. coli* that confer the ability to hydrolyze lactose—that is, no other protein, no other mutation in *E. coli* will work. Hall wrote:

> The phylogenetic evidence indicates that either Asp-92 and Cys/Trp-977 are the only acceptable amino acids at those positions, or that all of the single base substitutions that might be on the pathway to other amino acid replacements at those sites are so deleterious that they constitute a deep selective valley that has not been traversed in the 2 billion years since those proteins diverged from a common ancestor.[26]

Such results hardly support extravagant claims for the creativeness of Darwinian processes.

Another critical caveat not mentioned by Kenneth Miller is that the mutants that were initially isolated would be unable to use lactose in the wild—they required the artificial inducer IPTG to be present in the growth medium. Barry Hall states clearly that, in the absence of IPTG, no viable mutants are seen. The reason is that a permease is required to bring lactose into the cell. However, *ebg* only has a galactosidase activity, not a permease activity, so the experimental system had to rely on the pre-existing *lac* permease. Since the *lac* operon is repressed in the absence of either allolactose or IPTG, Hall decided to include the artificial inducer in all media up to this point so that the cells could grow. Thus, the system was being artificially supported by intelligent intervention.

The prose in Miller's book obscures the facts that most of the lactose system was already in place when the experiments began, that the system was carried through nonviable states by inclusion of IPTG, and that the system will not function without pre-existing components. From a skeptical perspective, the admirably careful work of Barry Hall involved a series of micromutations stitched together by intelligent intervention. He showed that the activity of a deleted enzyme could be replaced only by mutations to a second, homologous protein with a nearly-identical active site; and only if the second repressor already bound lactose; and only if the system were also artificially induced by IPTG; and only if the system were also allowed to use a preexisting permease. In my view, Hall's results are quite consistent with the idea that irreducible complexity requires intelligent intervention and that Darwinian processes cannot build complex systems.

Blood Clotting

A second putative counterexample to intelligent design concerns the blood clotting system. Blood clotting is a very intricate biochemical process, requiring many protein parts. I devoted a chapter of *Darwin's Black Box* to the blood clotting cascade, claiming that it is irreducibly complex and so does not fit well within a Darwinian framework. However, Russell Doolittle, a prominent biochemist, member of the National Academy of Sciences, and expert on blood clotting, disagreed. While discussing the similarity of the proteins of the blood clotting cascade to each other in an essay in *Boston Review* in 1997, he remarked that "the genes for new proteins come from the genes for old ones by gene duplication."[27] Doolittle's invocation of gene duplication has been repeated by many scientists reviewing my book, but it reflects a common confusion. Genes with similar sequences only suggest common descent — they do not speak to the mechanism of evolution. This point is critical to my argument and bears emphasis: *evidence of common descent is not evidence of natural selection*. Similarities among either organisms or proteins are the evidence for descent with modification, that is, for evolution. Natural selection, however, is a proposed explanation for how evolution might take place—its mechanism—and so it must be supported by other evidence if the question is not to be begged.

This point is critical to my argument and bears emphasis: evidence of common descent is not evidence of natural selection.

Doolittle then cited a paper by Bugge *et al* [28] entitled "Loss of fibrinogen rescues mice from the pleiotropic effects of plasminogen deficiency." By way of explanation, fibrinogen is the precursor of the clot material; plasminogen is a protein that degrades blood clots. He wrote:

> Recently, the gene for plaminogen [*sic*] was knocked out of mice, and, predictably, those mice had thrombotic complications because fibrin clots could not be cleared away. Not long after that, the same workers knocked out the gene for fibrinogen in another line of mice. Again, predictably, these mice were ailing, although in this case hemorrhage was the problem. And what do you think happened when these two lines of mice were crossed? For all practical purposes, the mice lacking both genes were normal! Contrary to claims about irreducible complexity, the entire ensemble of proteins is not needed. Music and harmony can arise from a smaller orchestra. [29]

The implied argument seems to be that the modern clotting system is actually not irreducibly complex, so a simpler clotting cascade might be missing factors such as plasminogen and fibrinogen, and perhaps it could be expanded into the modern clotting system by gene duplication. However, that interpretation does not stand up to a careful reading of Bugge *et al.*

In their paper, Bugge *et al.*[30] note that the lack of plasminogen in mice results in many problems, such as high mortality, ulcers, severe thrombosis, and delayed wound healing. On the other hand, lack of fibrinogen results in failure to clot, frequent hemorrhage, and death of females during pregnancy. The point of Bugge et al.[31] was that if one crosses the two knockout strains, producing plasminogen-plus-fibrinogen deficiency in individual mice, the mice do not suffer the many problems that afflict mice lacking plasminogen alone. Since the title of the paper emphasized that mice are "rescued" from some ill-effects, one might be misled into thinking that the double-knockout mice were normal. They are not. As Bugge et al.[32] state in their abstract, "Mice deficient in plasminogen and fibrinogen are phenotypically indistinguishable from fibrinogen-deficient mice." In other words, the double-knockouts have all the problems that mice lacking only fibrinogen have: they do not form clots, they hemorrhage, and the females die if they become pregnant. They are definitely not promising evolutionary intermediates.

The probable explanation is straightforward. The pathological symptoms of mice missing just plasminogen apparently are caused by uncleared clots. But fibrinogen-deficient mice cannot form clots in the first place. So problems due to uncleared clots don't arise either in fibrinogen-deficient mice or in mice that lack both plasminogen and fibrinogen. Nonetheless, the severe problems that attend lack of clotting in fibrinogen-deficient mice continue in the double knockouts. Pregnant females still perish.

Most important for the issue of irreducible complexity, however, is that the double-knockout mice do not merely have a less sophisticated, but still functional, clotting system. They have no functional clotting system at all. They are not evidence for the Darwinian evolution of blood clotting. Therefore, my argument, that the system is irreducibly complex, is unaffected by that example.

Other work from the same laboratory is consistent with the view that the blood clotting cascade is irreducibly complex. Experiments with "knock-out" mice in which the genes for other clotting components, called tissue factor and prothrombin, have been deleted separately, show that those components are required for clotting, and in their absence the organism suffers severely. (Bugge et al.[33]; Sun et al.[34])

Let me point out that two very competent scientists, Professors Miller and Doolittle, both of whom are highly motivated to discredit claims of intelligent design, and both of whom are quite capable of surveying the entire biomolecular literature for experimental counter-examples, both came up with examples which, when looked at skeptically, actually buttress the case for irreducible complexity, rather than weaken it. Of course, this does not prove that claims of irreducible complexity are true, or that intelligent design is correct.

Some scientists believe so strongly in Darwinism that their critical judgments are affected, and they will unconsciously overlook pretty obvious problems with Darwinian scenarios, or confidently assert things that are objectively untrue.

But, it demonstrates that scientists really don't have a handle on irreducible complexity, and that the idea of intelligent design is considerably stronger than its detractors would have us believe. It also shows the need to treat Darwinian scenarios, such as Miller and Doolittle offered, with a hermeneutic of suspicion. Some scientists believe so strongly in Darwinism that their critical judgments are affected, and they will unconsciously overlook pretty obvious problems with Darwinian scenarios, or confidently assert things that are objectively untrue.

Falsifiability

Let us now consider the issue of falsifiability. I know most philosophers of science do not regard falsifiability as a necessary trait of a successful scientific theory. Nonetheless, falsifiabilty is still an important factor to consider since it is nice to know whether or not one's theory can be shown to be wrong by contact with the real world.

A frequent charge made against intelligent design is that it is unfalsifiable, or untestable. For example, the National Academy of Sciences states: "[I]ntelligent design ... [is] not science because [it is] not testable by the methods of science."[35]

Yet, that claim seems to be at odds with the criticisms I just summarized. Clearly, Russell Doolittle and Kenneth Miller advanced scientific arguments aimed at falsifying Intelligent Design. If the results of Bugge et al.[36] had been as Doolittle first thought, or if Barry Hall's work had indeed shown what Miller implied, then they correctly believed my claims about irreducible complexity would have suffered quite a blow.

You cannot have it both ways. One cannot say both that intelligent design is unfalsifiable (or untestable) and that there is evidence against it. Either it is unfalsifiable and floats serenely beyond experimental reproach, or it can be criticized on the basis of our observations and is therefore testable. The fact that critical reviewers advance scientific arguments against intelligent design (whether successfully or not) shows that intelligent design is indeed falsifiable. It is open to falsification by a series of straightforward laboratory experiments such as those Miller and Doolittle cite and this is exactly why they pointed to them.

Now, ask how one could falsify the claim that a particular biochemical system was produced by a Darwinian process. Kenneth Miller announced that an "acid test" for the ability of natural selection to produce irreducible complexity. He then determined that natural selection passed the test and he unhesitatingly proclaimed intelligent design to be falsified and "Behe is wrong"[37]. But if, as it seems to me, *E. coli* actually fails the lactose-system "acid test," would Miller consider Darwinism to be falsified? Almost certainly not. He would surely say that Barry Hall started with the wrong bacterial species, or used the wrong selective pressure, and so on. So, Miller's "acid test" was not a test of Darwinism at all. Rather, it tested only intelligent design.

Intelligent design is quite susceptible to falsification, at least on the points under discussion. Darwinism, on the other hand, seems quite impervious to falsification.

The same one-way testing was employed by Russell Doolittle. He pointed to the results of Bugge *et al* to argue against intelligent design. But when the results turned out to be the opposite of what he had originally thought, Professor Doolittle did not abandon Darwinism.

It seems then, perhaps counterintuitively to some, that intelligent design is quite susceptible to falsification, at least on the points under discussion. Darwinism, on the other hand, seems quite impervious to falsification. The reason for that can be seen when we examine the basic claims of the two ideas with regard to a particular biochemical system like, say, the bacterial flagellum. The claim of intelligent design is that "*No* unintelligent process could produce this system." The claim of Darwinism is that "*Some* unintelligent process could produce this system." To falsify the first claim, one need only show that at least one unintelligent process could produce the system. To falsify the second claim, one would have to show the system could not have been formed by any of a potentially infinite number of possible unintelligent processes, which is effectively impossible to do.

The danger of accepting an effectively unfalsifiable hypothesis is that science has no way to determine if the belief corresponds to reality. In the history of science, the scientific community has believed in any number of things that were in fact not true or real, for example, the universal ether. If there were no way to test those beliefs, the progress of science might be substantially and negatively affected. In the present case, if the expansive claims of Darwinism are in reality not true, then its unfalsifiability can cause science to bog down in these areas, as I believe it has.

What can be done? I do not think the answer is to never investigate a theory that is unfalsifiable. After all, although it is unfalsifiable, Darwinism's claims are potentially positively demonstrable. For example, if some scientist conducted an experiment showing the production of a flagellum (or some equally complex system) by Darwinian processes, then the Darwinian claim would be affirmed. The question only arises in the face of negative results.

I propose several steps. First, one must be aware when a theory is unfalsifiable. Second, as far as possible, the advocate of an unfalsifiable theory should try diligently to positively demonstrate the claims of the hypothesis. Third, one needs to relax Darwin's criterion from this:

> If it could be demonstrated that any complex organ existed which could not possibly have been formed by numerous, successive, slight modifications, my theory would absolutely break down.[38]

to something like this:

> If a complex organ exists which seems *very unlikely* to have been produced by numerous, successive, slight modifications, and if no experiments have shown that it or comparable structures can be so produced, then maybe we're *barking up the wrong tree. So* ...

LET'S BREAK SOME RULES!

Of course, there will be those who differ on the point at which they decide to break rules. But, with the realistic criterion, there could be evidence against the unfalsifiable.

Then, scientists like Doolittle and Miller would run a risk when they cite an experiment that shows the opposite of what they had thought and science would have a way to escape from the rut of unfalsifiability to think new thoughts.

Then, scientists like Doolittle and Miller would run a risk when they cite an experiment that shows the opposite of what they had thought and science would have a way to escape from the rut of unfalsifiability and think new thoughts.

---

[1] Originally published in the journal *Philosophia Christi*, Series 2, 3 (2001).

[2] Maddox, John. "Down With the Big Bang." *Nature* 340 (1989).

[3] Darwin, C. *The Origin Of Species*. (New York: Bantam Books, 1859).

[4] Ibid., 154.

[5] Behe, M. J., *Darwin's Black Box: The Biochemical Challenge to Evolution*. (New York: The Free Press, 1996): 39.

[6] De Duve, C., *Vital Dust: Life As a Cosmic Imperative*.(New York: Basic Books, 1995): xiv.

[7] DeRosier, D. J., "The Turn of the Screw: The Bacterial Flagellar Motor." *Cell* 93 1998): 17-20.

[8] Special Issue on "Macromolecular Machines." *Cell* (6 February 1998).

[9] Ibid.

[10] Miller, K. R., *Finding Darwin's God: A Scientist's Search for Common Ground Between God and Evolution*. (New York: Cliff Street Books, 1999).

[11] Miller, K. R., *Finding Darwin's God: A Scientist's Search for Common Ground Between God and Evolution*. (New York: Cliff Street Books, 1999). National Academy of Sciences, *Science and Creationism: A View From the National Academy of Sciences*, (Washington DC: National Academy Press, 1999).

[12] Hall, B. G., *Evolution on a Petri Dish: The Evolved b-galactosidase System as a Model for Studying Acquisitive Evolution in the Laboratory*. In "Evolutionary Biology". M. K. Hecht, B. Wallace, and G. T. PranceEds. (New York: Plenum Press, 1982b): 85-150.

[13] Miller, K. R., *Finding Darwin's God: A Scientist's Search for Common Ground Between God and Evolution*. (New York: Cliff Street Books, 1999). National Academy of Sciences, Science and Creationism: A View from the National Academy of Sciences. (Washington DC: National Academy Press, 1999): 146-147.

[14] Hall, B. G., "Experimental Evolution of Ebg Enzyme Provides Clues about the Evolution of Catalysis and to Evolutionary Potential," *FEMS Microbiology Letters* 174 (1999): 1-8.

[15] Hall, B. G., "Evolution of a Regulated Operon in the Laboratory. *Genetics* 101 (1982a): 335-344.

[16] Hall, B. G., *Evolution on a Petri Dish: The Evolved ?-galactosidase System as a Model for Studying Acquisitive Evolution in the Laboratory*. In "Evolutionary Biology". M. K. Hecht, B. Wallace, and G. T. PranceEds. (New York: Plenum Press, 1982b): 85-150.

[17] Cairns, J., "Mutation and Cancer: The Antecedents to Our Studies of Adaptive Mutation," *Genetics* 148 (1998): 1433-1440.

[18] Foster, P. L., "Mechanisms of Stationary Phase Mutation: A Decade of Adaptive Mutation," *Annual Review of Genetics* 33 (1999): 57-88.

[19] Hall, B. G., "Adaptive Mutagenesis: A Process That Generates Almost Exclusively Beneficial Mutations," *Genetica* 102-103 (1998): 109-125.

[20] McFadden, J. and Al Khalili, J. (1999). "A Quantum Mechanical Model of Adaptive Mutation. *Biosystem.* 50 (1999): 203-211.

[21] Shapiro, J. A., "Genome Organization, Natural Genetic Engineering and Adaptive Mutation," *Trends in Genetics* 13 (1997): 98-104.

[22] Hall, B. G., "On The Specificity of Adaptive Mutations," *Genetics* 145 (1997): 39-44.

[23] Hall, B. G., "Evolution of a Regulated Operon in the Laboratory. *Genetics* 101 (1982a): 335-344.

[24] Hall, B. G. "Experimental Evolution of Ebg Enzyme Provides Clues About the Evolution of Catalysis and to Evolutionary Potential," *FEMS Microbiology Letters* 174 (1999): 1-8.

[25] Ibid.

[26] Ibid.

[27] Doolittle, R. F., "A Delicate Balance," *Boston Review*, Feb/March (1997): 28-29.

[28] Bugge, T. H., Kombrinck, K. W., Flick, M. J., Daugherty, C. C., Danton, M. J., and Degen, J. L., "Loss of Fibrinogen Rescues Mice From the Pleiotropic Effects of Plasminogen Deficiency," *Cell* 87 (1996a): 709-719.

[29] Doolittle, R. F., "A Delicate Balance". *Boston Review*, Feb/March (1997): 28-29.

[30] Bugge, T. H., Kombrinck, K. W., Flick, M. J., Daugherty, C. C., Danton, M. J., and Degen, J. L., "Loss of Fibrinogen Rescues Mice From the Pleiotropic Effects of Plasminogen Deficiency," *Cell.* 87 (1996a): 709-719.

[31] Ibid.

[32] Ibid.

[33] Bugge, T. H., Xiao, Q., Kombrinck, K. W., Flick, M. J., Holmback, K., Danton, M. J., Colbert, M. C., Witte, D. P., Fujikawa, K., Davie, E. W., and Degen, J. L., "Fatal Embryonic Bleeding Events in Mice Lacking Tissue Factor, The Cell- Associated Initiator of Blood Coagulation," *Proceedings of the National Academy of Sciences of the United States of America* 93 (1996b): 6258-6263.

[34] Sun, W. Y., Witte, D. P., Degen, J. L., Colbert, M. C., Burkart, M. C., Holmback, K., Xiao, Q., Bugge, T. H., and Degen, S. J. (1998). "Prothrombin Deficiency Results in Eembryonic and Neonatal Lethality in Mice," *Proceedings of the National Academy of Sciences of the United States of America* 95 (1998): 7597-7602.

[35] *Science and Creationism* booklet printed by the National Academy of Sciences (1999): 25.

[36] Bugge, T. H., Kombrinck, K. W., Flick, M. J., Daugherty, C. C., Danton, M. J., and Degen, J. L., "Loss of Fibrinogen Rescues Mice From the Pleiotropic Effects of Plasminogen Deficiency," *Cell.* 87 (1996a): 709-719.

[37] Miller, K. R., *Finding Darwin's God: A Scientist's Search for Common Ground Between God and Evolution* (New York: Cliff Street Books, 1999):147. National Academy of Sciences (1999). *Science and Creationism: A View from the National Academy of Sciences.* (Washington DC: National Academy Press; 1984).

[38] Darwin, C.,154.

PART IV:

THE FUTURE OF SCIENCE

Chapter Eight

—◦◦◦—

MODERN SCIENCE: CHARTING A COURSE FOR THE FUTURE

Wesley D. Allen

Dr. Wesley Allen is a research professor at the Center for Computational Quantum Chemistry at the University of Georgia. He earned a B.A. in Chemistry and Physics from Vanderbilt University and a Ph.D. in Theoretical Chemistry from the University of California at Berkeley. He has authored over 50 publications in the scientific literature.

Abstract

It is argued here that a grounding in the Christian worldview can preserve the vitality and veracity of the scientific enterprise in the new millennium. Four concepts are discussed that have their roots in centuries past and that ought to be reclaimed, even rediscovered, in the context of 21st century scientific culture: (1) the Christian heritage and raison d'être of modern science dating back to its birthplace in Europe, (2) a proper exercise of human dominion commissioned by God over creation, (3) the exquisite designs and forms of the laws of nature, and (4) a philosophical understanding of methodological naturalism in order to safeguard the foundation of the scientific disciplines. Several contemporary research topics in science are identified in which a strong interplay with Christian perspectives is inherent. In summary, the essay develops principles to be used by Christians to influence scientific discourse, and then it identifies specific areas of current intellectual development that not only provide challenge and stimulation for Christian scholarship, but also can be shaped by the Christian worldview.

CHARTING A COURSE FOR A NEW MILLENNIUM in science is a humbling task, perhaps to be undertaken only by those with a high degree of temerity. At the start of the last millennium, despite thousands of years of human civilization, there was no organized science, and not even the rudiments of the modern university were in existence. The structure of the solar system was misunderstood. The chemical elements were unknown. There was no concept of identifying and formulating the physical forces of nature. Mathematical methods for physics did not exist, as calculus would not be invented for almost 700 years. Even more time would be required to unravel pathogenesis.

Charting a Course for the Future

The year 2000 marks the centennial of the birth of modern physics, which is often traced to the theoretical work presented by Max Planck in the fall of 1900 to the German Physical Society on the black-body radiation problem—a seemingly obscure enigma that caused scientists to stumble onto quantum mechanics, the area of my professional expertise. Notwithstanding the monumental achievements of Newton, Joule, Kelvin, Boltzmann, Faraday, Maxwell and many others, even the turn of the last century now seems a period of primitive scientific understanding. The structure of the atom remained a mystery. There was virtually complete ignorance about biochemistry; for example, elucidation of the structure and function of DNA by Watson and Crick did not occur until the 1950s. General and special relativity had not yet revealed the basic fabric of space and time. Big Bang cosmology had yet to make its splash. There were no antibiotics. Innumerable materials such as plastics, which are taken for granted in modern households, awaited discovery and marketing. Airplanes, much less spacecraft, had never been constructed. Finally, there were no computers! In view of these astounding developments of the last century, it is prudent to eschew speculation or extrapolation about the new discoveries science will yield in the coming decades. Indeed, many entertaining articles making more or less serious attempts to predict the technological future of human society appeared in popular news magazines around the advent of the year 2000.

By contrast, some timeless principles grounded in a Christian worldview are advanced in this essay to help preserve the vitality and veracity of scientific enterprise in the new millennium.

By contrast, some timeless principles grounded in a Christian worldview are advanced in this essay to help preserve the vitality and veracity of scientific enterprise in the new millennium. However, some contextual remarks dealing with broad personal issues are warranted first.

Nurturing People Around Us

In our modern society, the explosion of scientific knowledge and technological change is a source of exuberance to some, but rootlessness and angst to others. Most Christians recognize the relational and often one-to-one context for Christian witness, whether they are actively engaged in this calling or not. The university years are a time of high anxiety for most students. According to a 1990s survey[1] of graduate students in the US, the most crippling anxiety students experience is the struggle to achieve balance in their lives. The survey clearly showed that although grad students are gratified by their academic achievement, many fear they may be transformed into academic automatons, missing the experience of "real life" outside the classroom or library, often at the expense of their health. Despite their stated priority of personal relationships, many graduate students found their friendships unfulfilling, one of the costs of the unwavering goal of educational success. The impact of the gospel and a relationship with Christ is always more vivid when modeled in the lives of professionals whom students respect. Scripture is replete with inspiration and instruction relevant to this setting:

No, in all these things we are more than conquerors through him who loved us. For I am convinced that neither death nor life, neither angels nor demons, neither the present nor the future, nor anything else in all creation, will be able to separate us from the love of God that is in Christ Jesus our Lord. (Romans 8:37-39, NIV)

Do not let any unwholesome talk come out of your mouths, but only what is helpful for building others up according to their needs, that it may benefit those who listen. Get rid of all bitterness, rage and anger, brawling and slander, along with every form of malice. Be kind and compassionate to one another, forgiving each other, just as in Christ, God forgave you. Be imitators of God, therefore, as dearly loved children and live a life of love, just as Christ loved us and gave himself up for us as a fragrant offering and sacrifice to God. (Ephesians 4:29, 31-32; 5:1, 2, NIV)

Excellence in scholarship and scientific discovery must be a *complement* to rather than a *substitute for* living a life of love as an imitator of God, a foundation for the type of professionalism about which Scripture repeatedly reminds us.

Escape from Collective Hopelessness

In addition to addressing the plight of *individuals*, Christianity also clearly provides for a more *collective* escape from postmodern nihilism or hopelessness. It often strikes me that, in the absence of Christian hope, scientific findings themselves can accelerate the slide into the abyss of meaninglessness. Darwinism is not particularly what I have in mind here, but I am referring to the natural fate of the Earth being discovered by astrophysicists and geoscientists.

A popular report[2] on this topic caught my attention in early 2000 during a symposium at the national meeting of the American Association for the Advancement of Science. The natural fate of the

Earth depends on the sun, which, like any other star, will not last forever. In the evolution of its nuclear fusion processes, the sun is gradually getting brighter and hotter. Eventually, this process will raise the Earth's temperature above levels that can support life—no matter what efforts are taken to avert global warming by reducing greenhouse gas emissions.

According to James F. Kasting, Professor of Geosciences at Pennsylvania State University, the Earth will start losing its water at 140° F, when water vapor rises into the stratosphere in huge quantities and breaks down chemically, losing its hydrogen into space. New models suggest that the oceans will disappear and the Earth will be a waterless desert within 1.2 billion years, but trouble with carbon dioxide sequestering in warm oceans could occur much earlier. Kasting said, "If we calculated correctly, Earth has been habitable for 4.5 billion years and only has a half billion left." This scenario assumes that life on Earth is not destroyed in the meantime by a collision with a meteorite greater than 10 km in diameter, an event that is not implausible over a time scale of several hundred million years. In fact, in accord with the Rare Earth hypothesis[3] advocated by prominent astrobiologists, there are numerous conditions on our planet and in our solar system that are finely tuned for the existence of animal life on Earth, but are subject to failure over geologic time scales. These remarkable conditions include the Earth's spin rate; its stable axis of rotation mediated by an abnormally large moon; its nearly circular orbit in the habitable zone about the sun; its protection from asteroid and comet impacts by the gravitational field of Jupiter; its dearth of massive cosmic radiation showers from supernovae or neutron stars; its protective magnetic field arising from a molten iron core; and its built-in global thermostat functioning via the regulation of greenhouse gases by plate tectonics.

Science will undoubtedly continue to identify and substantiate natural threats to human existence, but the fact remains that the human race faces cosmic hopelessness apart from the Christian gospel.

A frighteningly vulnerable Earth in an exceedingly hostile universe is too disconcerting to publicize on most cable television nature shows.

Nevertheless, most people have flippant disregard for the grim natural fate that appears to await the Earth, because this scenario seems so far removed from our lifetimes. Science will undoubtedly continue to identify and substantiate natural threats to human existence, but the fact remains that the human race faces cosmic hopelessness apart from the Christian gospel.

A Christian Vision for Modern Science

Having identified some individual and collective ways Christianity can impact the scientific community, one wonders if it is possible to develop a comprehensive Christian vision for science. I suggest here that there is indeed a vision that offers a fruitful interface between science and Christianity. While these ideas have their roots in centuries past, we must reclaim— and perhaps even rediscover—them in our 21st century academic culture. These points can be summarized in four words: heritage, dominion, form, and safeguard.

Heritage

Organized science is an invented cultural institution, not present in all societies, and not one that may be counted upon to arise from human instinct. Virtually all human societies have exhibited some level of *natural philosophy* (speculations about the natural world) and *manual arts* (technical skills such as metallurgy or means of navigation). However, as argued in *The Soul of Science* by Pearcey and Thaxton,[4] science as a discipline demands some kind of unique soil in which to flourish. Deprived of that soil, it is as capable of decay and death as any other human activity. Christianized Europe was the birthplace of modern science—there and nowhere else, and not by accident. It is the Christian worldview that gave birth in an articulate fashion to the experimental method of science itself. It was Christianity that first gave faith in the very *possibility* of science, a necessary antecedent to the development of organized scientific enterprise. In more recent times, anti-religious polemics and exaggerations of some notable conflicts between church leaders and prominent scientists have confused, or even severed, this connection in the public mind. Yet the historical model that Pearcey and Thaxton have presented is one which, I believe, must be preserved in the academy, not necessarily institutionally, but in effective individual practice.

This rich heritage is based on several tenets, which taken together are distinctive of Christianity:

a) The universe is real, not illusory, the product of a God whose character is immutable. This tenet is at variance with pantheistic notions that place inherent distrust in sensory experience in an unpredictable world.

b) Nature, being divinely created, is of inherent worth and thus *worthy* of study. This conclusion supplants any *Zeitgeist* that would view science as a mere intellectual pastime.

c) Nature itself is not divine, and thus humanity may probe it free of fear—an important realization in early eras dominated by superstitions about the natural environment. Worship and ultimate reverence are reserved for the Creator, not for the creation nor for humans as creatures therein.

d) Humankind, formed in the image of God, can discover order in the universe by rational interpretation (*i.e.*, the codes of nature *can* be unveiled and read). Without this faith, science would have never been developed because the very practice of it would be impossible in principle.

e) The form of nature is not inherent within nature, but its form is from a divine command imposed from outside nature. Thus, the details of the world must first be uncovered by observation rather than mere rational musing, because God is free to create according to His own purposes. In this way science was liberated from Aristotelian rationalism, whereby the Creator was subjected to the dictates of reason constructed by humans. Such Gnosticism, which transformed speculation into dogma, undermined the open-endedness of science.[5] To be sure, Christianity holds that God is a perfectly rational being who cannot act inconsistently with His character, but this principle only places partial con straints on His creative activity, which science must be free to discover in all its diversity.

Perusing human history reminds us that progress in science and technology is not a monotonically increasing function of time. There are periods, due to political, social, natural or other calamities, or merely shifts, in which information or scientific expertise is temporarily or irretrievably lost. In addition to the fall of numerous great empires of antiquity, there are examples of such declines that have occurred within the last generation, most notably the collapse of organized science in the former Soviet Union and the continuing flight of top Eastern European scientists to Western countries.

As scientists, we must realize that it is possible for certain fields to become moribund within a few short years. Many research professors in the United States rightly worry about the lack of quality graduate students in many scientific disciplines. In my field, I am concerned that there are too few students adequately prepared in mathematics and physics to be living repositories of the great advances and classic papers of quantum chemistry over the past 75 years. It is regrettable, but common, in research for a massive computer code for quantum chemical computations, developed with great effort, to languish as an unintelligible morass once the original authors have earned their degrees and passed onward without having competent junior graduate students present to adopt their projects.

Clearly, a postmodern culture devoid of absolute truths and rules of logic does not provide this vital medium. I contend that in properly grasping our Christian heritage and the tenets it embodies, this medium can be preserved.

In brief, we need to be concerned about maintaining a milieu that provides the right soil for science to flourish, one not only in which a substantial fraction of young people are capable of thinking in analytic depth, rather than in sound bites, but also one in which many feel a deep calling to practice science. Clearly, a postmodern culture devoid of absolute truths and rules of logic does not provide this vital medium. I contend that in properly grasping our Christian heritage and the tenets it embodies, this medium can be preserved. This message needs to be heard in both the academy and in our churches, where anti-scientific opinions are often as severe as the anti-Christian bias prevailing in the modern university.

Dominion

The Christian heritage of science is also integrally connected with the idea of dominion. Over the centuries Christians have found biblical justification for an active use of nature in the creation account (Genesis 1:28), where God gives human beings "dominion" over the earth. By mastering through science the principles instituted in nature, this commission becomes fully realizable, and stewardship becomes essential. Accordingly, from its first days the goal of science was to glorify God and benefit mankind. In 1605 Francis Bacon published a small book called *The Advancement of Learning*, which proved instrumental in establishing science as a socially accepted institution. According to Bacon,

> . . . let no man, upon a weak conceit of sobriety or an ill-applied moderation, think or maintain that a man can search too far or be too well studied in the book of God's word or in the book of God's works; divinity or philosophy; but rather let men endeavor an endless progress or proficience (*sic*) in both; only let men beware that they apply both to charity, and not to swelling; to use, and not to ostentation; and again, that they do not unwisely mingle or confound these learnings together.[6]

Bacon's rhetoric thus propounded the *two books doctrine*: the Bible was one of God's revelations, the Book of God's Word, but nature was a second revelation, the Book of God's Works. This doctrine placed the study of God's works in nature as an act of worship conjoined with the study of God's Word, the Scriptures. To adapt this principle to proper theological terms, it should be understood as the compatibility and utility of science as general revelation *vis-à-vis* the Scriptures as special revelation. Biblical grounding for this view can be found, among other places, in Psalm 19:1-4 (NIV):

The heavens declare the glory of God; the skies proclaim the work of his hands. Day after day they pour forth speech; night after night they display knowledge. There is no speech or language where their voice is not heard. Their voice goes out into all the earth, their words to the ends of the world.

In 1654, John Cotton provided further advocacy for the "two books" doctrine, saying, "to study the nature and course and use of all God's works is a duty imposed by God."[7] In my view, it is here that science and technology find their *raison d'être*, a justification that is essentially timeless and certainly still viable in the new millennium.

In recapturing the concept of dominion, and of science as an act of rational (rather than mystical) worship, Christians find abundant humanitarian motivation. Indeed, note that Bacon provided an enduring ethos for science by insisting that scientific work be performed in the spirit of *agape* love ("charity" in Elizabethan English), combating the ever-present Faustian temptation to sell one's soul for worldly gain. It is striking how accurate Bacon's concern turned out to be in the 20th century, which was dominated by technology-assisted world wars, totalitarian suppression, and nuclear threats. To avert even greater humanitarian disasters in the new millennium and to use science judiciously for the benefit of mankind, I can think of no better guiding principle than the Christian ideals popularized by Bacon four centuries ago.

In this light, the distinguishing character of science that is truly and fully Christian should be excellence of scholarship, in accord with basic standards of evidence and detached argument, and in fairness toward opposing views.

The concept of science as an act of worship and a reading and subsequent rendering of God's general revelation also provides exceedingly high standards for academic research and scholarship. In the modern academy, there are enormous pressures to publish volumes of populist research, often at the expense of careful scientific procedures and thoughtful analyses. If publishing a scientific paper is to be an act of dominion and worship, then it must be the best scholarship possible. In this light, the distinguishing character of science that is truly and fully Christian should be excellence of scholarship, in accord with basic standards of evidence and detached argument, and in fairness toward opposing views. We should keep in mind Colossians 3:23-24 (NIV):

> Whatever you do, work at it with all your heart, as working for the Lord, not for men, since you know that you will receive an inheritance from the Lord as a reward. It is the Lord Christ you are serving.

Form

Additional aspects of the Christian worldview lead to a third broad topic: Form—with a capital F, in the (neo) Platonic sense of the word. In the Christian worldview, the universe is an orderly world (a *cosmos*) crafted by a rational God, not a capricious, *lawless* entity. Natural occurrences are *lawful* and intelligible, and they may be described in the beauty and exactitude of mathematics. The conviction that all phenomena of nature should follow a master plan because God has designed the universe according to his perfect character was a central motivation of Copernicus, Kepler, Galileo, and Newton.[8] Despite common misperceptions, the conflict between some of these scientific luminaries and the established church was not rooted in basic Christian theology itself, but rather in the widespread influence that Aristotelian philosophy had gained in the church in the late Middle Ages.[9] Galileo is noted for his statement that the book of nature is written by the hand of God in the language of mathematics. This theme is echoed in the words of Kepler.

> The chief aim of all investigations of the external world should be to discover the rational order and harmony which has been imposed on it by God and which He revealed to us in the language of mathematics.[10]

The question of design in the universe, as seen in the mathematical laws of nature, is discussed at greater length in other essays in this book.

In my view, the mathematical laws of physics embody the Forms of reality instituted by God and are not merely human attempts to approximate, or model, reality. My research is based on the laws of quantum physics, as applied to chemical phenomena, which appear to be subject to these Forms in totality. In our field, enormous computational effort is invested toward achieving ever more accurate numerical solutions to these equations of physics, in pursuit of God's answers, if you will. A famous quotation by the eminent physicist and Nobelist P. A. M. Dirac in 1929 summarizes this continuing pursuit:

> The underlying physical laws necessary for the mathematical theory of a large part of physics and the whole of chemistry are thus completely known, and the difficulty is only that the exact application of these laws leads to equations much too complicated to be soluble.[11]

I know of no better demonstration of order and design in the universe than witnessing the laws of quantum mechanics yielding 4, 5, 6 or even (in principle) many more digits of accuracy in predicting energy levels, structures, and properties of molecules never even seen by the theorist at work, and perhaps never previously observed by mankind. I stand in no less awe of these equations than when I first encountered their incredible validity as an undergraduate student.

I know of no better demonstration of order and design in the universe than witnessing the laws of quantum mechanics....

Quantum mechanics has been termed "the champion of physical theories" and is arguably the most successful mathematical framework for the description of nature ever discovered. Nick Herbert offers a vivid portrayal of this triumph of physics, which ironically arose from muddled beginnings:

Quantum theory was devised in the late twenties to deal with the atom, a tiny entity a thousand times smaller than the wavelength of green light. Disturbed by its philosophical implications, many physicists at that time considered quantum theory a provisional device bound to fail outside the atomic realm. Quantum theory continued, however, to prosper beyond its inventors' wildest dreams, resolving subtle problems of atomic structure, tackling the nucleus some ten thousand times smaller than the atom itself, and then extending its reach to the realm of the elementary particles (quarks, gluons, leptons) which many believe to be the world's ultimate constituents. With each success quantum theory became more audacious . . . . Heaping success upon success, quantum theory boldly exposes itself to potential falsification on a thousand different fronts. Its record is impressive: quantum theory passes every test we can devise. After sixty years of play, this theory is still batting a thousand.[12]

In this description the success of quantum theory is clearly not ascribed to the brilliance of its inventors, and seemingly for lack of a comfortable alternative, the theory itself is personified and given volition of its own. But quantum theory is a Form, not a physical entity endowed with power. Its remarkable validity speaks clearly of the character of the Creator who brought it into being and holds it in existence.

Safeguard

A fourth aspect of a Christian vision for science is the safeguarding of the scientific disciplines as an act of stewardship and dominion. To be sure, a key aspect of this enterprise involves entering into and influencing contemporary debates over scientific and technological ethics. The issues seem only to burgeon with time: nuclear weapons and technologies, genetic engineering, cloning, toxicology, and environmentalism, to name a few. I certainly do not claim that all Christians should be in agreement on all these issues, or that it is always clear how to apply our faith to each dilemma. I am saying that we should extend the concept of dominion to include active concern for maintaining rectitude in the scientific enterprise.

But there is a second sense of safeguard I have in mind—ensuring a proper philosophical grounding of science. In *Reason in the Balance*,[13] Phillip Johnson argues forcefully that there is a dogmatic religious philosophy in contemporary culture, certainly not Christianity, but rather the metaphysical doctrines of scientific naturalism and liberal rationalism. Both hold that nature is all there is, a permanently closed system of material causes and effects that can never be influenced by anything outside of itself. Humans are therefore free to create their own standards of science and society according to practical experience, or often according to expediency. Because Christianity can provide an external critique of naturalism as a metaphysical doctrine, it is able to safeguard science from poorly examined "just so" stories, necessitated for lack of viable alternatives, which demand acceptance of improbable naturalistic explanations of complex phenomena. When science addresses larger issues in this vein, such as the origin of the universe and the origin of life, the public at large does not possess sufficient technical knowledge to judge whether or not claims are extravagant. The safeguard of Christianity is thus not to reject as a matter of course a given naturalistic theory, but rather to demand a proper burden of scientific proof from its proponents.

The safeguard of Christianity is thus not to reject as a matter of course a given naturalistic theory, but rather to demand a proper burden of scientific proof from its proponents.

Myriad examples in daily life of metaphysical doctrines parading as scientific fact become apparent to discerning minds freed from emotional and philosophical commitments to naturalism. The influential series *Cosmos* by Carl Sagan opens with the bald claim: "The Cosmos is all that is or ever was or ever will be," a premise disguised as scientific conclusion to the general public.[14] Moreover, in a recent commentary in *Time* magazine on the Kansas Board of Education controversy, Stephen

Jay Gould asserts that "evolution is as well documented as any phenomenon in science, as strongly as the earth's revolution around the sun rather than vice versa."[15] To be fair, one should first demand that Gould define precisely what he means by the term "evolution," but the context is clearly that of large-scale evolution across species. As such, even those who find the physical evidence for macroevolution compelling ought to decry this statement as outrageous misrepresentation. A wry account of another example comprises an essay by Phillip Johnson on the 1995 "Statement on Teaching Evolution" promulgated by the U.S. National Association of Biology Teachers, whereby the possibility of divine supervision over evolution was insidiously excluded.[16] Finally, the work of Lehigh University biochemist Michael Behe is laudable in holding Darwinian origin of life theories to higher evidential standards in the face of the enormous roadblocks to gradualism posed by apparent, pervasive irreducible complexity in biochemical systems. According to Behe,

> None of the papers published in *JME* [Journal of Molecular Evolution] over the entire course of its life as a journal [since 1971] has ever proposed a detailed model by which a complex biochemical system might have been produced in a gradual, step-by-step Darwinian fashion. Although many scientists ask how sequences change or how chemicals necessary for life might be produced in the absence of cells, no one has ever asked in the pages of *JME* such questions as the following: How did the photosynthetic reaction center develop? How did intramolecular transport start? How did cholesterol biosynthesis begin? How did retinal become involved in vision? How did phosphoprotein signaling pathways develop? The very fact that none of these problems is even addressed, let alone solved, is a very strong indication that Darwinism is an inadequate framework for understanding the origin of complex biochemical systems.[17]

In principle, criticisms such as Behe's, serve to safeguard the veracity of the sciences, but they should also come from those committed to metaphysical naturalism. At times, strong objections do arise from naturalistic quarters, however, experience reveals too many cases to the contrary, such as the examples just given. Just as politics is too important to be left to the politicians, science is too important to be policed only by those having the same philosophical commitments, particularly commitments that hubristically elevate humans as ultimate adjudicators. Thus, those professing the Christian worldview have a key role to play in a constructive system of checks and balances within the scientific community.

A Charge to Fulfill

My views as a scientist revolve around a Christian vision of heritage, dominion, form, and safeguard – concepts on which science was built and concepts that will preserve its efficacy and integrity into the future. These guiding principles can provide Christians with inspiration in the daily practice of science, which often seems mundane and devoid of real value. For society at large, they provide a model of the complementarity of science and Christianity, contrary to the destructive cultural wars perceived by many as inescapable, and actively propagated by some as essential to ideological purity. In accord with Scriptural mandates, these guiding principles for science must be accompanied by personal actions that emulate the love of Christ, nurture confused or hurting individuals, and provide for an escape from the collective hopelessness of a postmodern culture. What is needed now is a generation of Christians called into the scientific disciplines, who have reclaimed these timeless principles and who stand convicted by them in individual practice.

With such an abundance of areas for the fruitful interplay of science and Christianity at the turn of this new millennium, it is quite apparent that Christians have a vast charge to fulfill.

There are a number of specific, contemporary scientific issues that not only provide challenge and stimulation for Christian scholarship, but that can also be shaped by the Christian worldview. Space constraints prevent any of these themes from being developed here at the end of this essay, but in the interest of equipping Christians to grapple with the key issues of concern, it is worthwhile to provide some helpful literature sources written from both Christian and secular perspectives. A limited list of topics and references is as follows: general Christian scholarship in the modern academy;[18] the philosophy of science and contemporary culture;[19] Big Bang cosmology and the origins of the universe;[20] intelligent design in the universe;[21] chaos, complexity, and God—issues of determinism, chance, and providence in human existence;[22] interpretations of quantum mechanics—the nature of microscopic reality;[23] God and man in space-time—considerations of special and general relativity;[24] the existence of higher dimensionality in the universe—synthesis of quantum mechanics and general relativity via string theory;[25] biochemical design and irreducible complexity in *Darwin's Black Box*—challenges to orthodox theories of evolution.[26] With such an abundance of areas for the fruitful interplay of science and Christianity at the turn of this new millennium, it is quite apparent that Christians have a vast charge to fulfill. The question is whether we will exercise the concepts of heritage, dominion, form, and safeguard in making a genuine impact that will further the cause of Christ.

---

[1] Barna, George. "Understanding Graduate Students: Their Values, Beliefs, and Motivations," available at the Grad Resources website at http://www.gradresource.org/articles/student_profile.shtml

[2] "Grim Fate Awaits Earth, Scientists Say," *USA Today*, 20 February 2000.

[3] Ward, P.D. and D. Brownlee, *Rare Earth: Why Complex Life Is Uncommon in the Universe* (New York: Copernicus, 2000).

[4] Pearcey, N.R. and C. B. Thaxton, *The Soul of Science: Christian Faith and Natural Philosophy* (Wheaton, IL: Crossway Books, 1994).

[5] Lessl, T.M. "Francis Bacon and the Biblical Origins of the Scientific Ethos," *Communication and Religion* 15 (1992): 87.

[6] Ibid.

[7] Pearcey and Thaxton, *The Soul of Science*, 35.

[8] Kline, M. *Mathematics in Western Culture* (New York: Oxford University Press, 1953); M. Kline, *Mathematics: The Loss of Certainty* (New York: Oxford University Press, 1980). See also Pearcey and Thaxton, *The Soul of Science*.

[9] In chapter 1 of *The Soul of Science*, Pearcey and Thaxton elucidate the historical issues behind the controversy between Galileo and the Roman Catholic Church.

10 Kline, M. *Mathematics: The Loss of Certainty*, 31.

11 Dirac, P.A.M. Proceedings of the Royal Society 123 (1929): 714.

12 Herbert, N. *Quantum Reality* (New York: Anchor Books, 1985).

13 Johnson, Philip E. *Reason in the Balance: The Case Against Naturalism in Science, Law, and Culture* (Downers Grove, IL: InterVarsity Press, 1995).

14 Sagan, Carl. *Cosmos* (New York: Ballantine, 1985): 1.

15 "Dorothy, It's Really Oz," *Time* 23 August 1999.

16 Johnson, Philip E. *Objections Sustained: Subversive Essays on Evolution, Law, and Culture* (Downers Grove, IL: InterVarsity Press, 1998).

17 Behe, Michael J. *Darwin's Black Box: The Biochemical Challenge to Evolution* (New York: Free Press, 1996).

18 Marsden, G. M. *The Outrageous Idea of Christian Scholarship* (New York: Oxford University Press, 1997); Marsden, G. M. *The Soul of the American University* (New York: Oxford University Press, 1994).

19 Johnson, Philip E. *Reason in the Balance*; P. E. Johnson, *Objections Sustained*; Moreland, J. P. *Christianity and the Nature of Science* (Grand Rapids: Baker, 1989); Ratzsch, D. *Philosophy of Science: The Natural Sciences in Christian Perspective* (Downers Grove, IL: InterVarsity Press, 1986); Moreland, J. P. ed., *The Creation Hypothesis: Scientific Evidence for an Intelligent Designer* (Downers Grove, IL: InterVarsity Press, 1994); Kuhn, T. *The Structure of Scientific Revolutions* (Chicago: University of Chicago Press, 1962); Gould, S. J. *Rocks of Ages: Science and Religion in the Fullness of Life* (New York: Ballantine, 1999).

20 Ross, Hugh. *The Creator and the Cosmos* (Colorado Springs: Navpress, 1993); Ross, Hugh. *Beyond the Cosmos* (Colorado Springs: NavPress, 1996); Craig, William L. and Q. Smith, *Theism, Atheism, and Big Bang Cosmology* (Oxford: Clarendon Press, 1993); Davies, P. *God and the New Physics* (New York: Touchstone Books, 1984); Hawking, Stephen. *A Brief History of Time* (New York: Bantam, 1988).

21 Behe, *Darwin's Black Box*; Moreland, *The Creation Hypothesis*; Ross, *The Creator and the Cosmos*; Davies, *God and the New Physics*; Dembski, W. A. *Intelligent Design: The Bridge between Science and Theology* (Downers Grove, IL: InterVarsity Press, 1999); Overman, D. L. *A Case Against Accident and Self-Organization* (New York: Rowman & Littlefield, 1997).

22 Overman, *A Case Against Accident and Self-Organization;* Russell, R. J., N. Murphy, and A. R. Peacocke, ed. *Chaos and Complexity: Scientific Perspectives on Divine Action*, (Vatican City: Vatican Observatory, 1995); Davis, J. J. "Theological Reflections on Chaos Theory," *Perspectives on Science and Christian Faith* 49 (1997): 75; Williams, G. P. *Chaos Theory Tamed* (Washington, DC: Joseph Henry Press, 1997); Coveney, P. and R. Highfield, *Frontiers of Complexity: The Search for Order in a Chaotic World* (New York: Fawcett, 1995); Gleick, J. *Chaos: Making a New Science* (New York: Penguin, 1987); Stewart, I. *Does God Play Dice? The Mathematics of Chaos* (Oxford: Blackwell, 1989); Kauffman, S. *At Home in the Universe* (New York: Oxford University Press, 1995).

23 Pearcey and Thaxton, *The Soul of Science*; Herbert, N. *Quantum Reality* (New York: Anchor Books, 1985); Davies, P. C. W., and J. R. Brown, ed. *The Ghost in the Atom*, (Cambridge: Cambridge University Press, 1999); Gribbin, J. Schrödinger's *Kittens and*

the Search for Reality (Boston: Back Bay Books, 1995); Penrose, R. *Shadows of the Mind* (New York: Oxford University Press, 1994); Penrose, R. *The Large, the Small, and the Human Mind* (Cambridge: Cambridge University Press, 1997); Capra, F. *The Tao of Physics* (New York: Bantam, 1977); Zukav, G. *The Dancing Wu Li Masters* (New York: Bantam, 1980).

[24]Pearcey and Thaxton, *The Soul of Science*; Penrose, *The Large, the Small, and the Human Mind* ; Thorne, K S. *Black Holes and Time Warps* (New York: W. W. Norton, 1994).

[25] Ross, *Beyond the Cosmos*; Greene, B. *The Elegant Universe* (New York: Vintage Books, 1999); Kaku, M. Hyperspace (New York: Anchor Books, 1995).

[26] Pearcey and Thaxton, *The Soul of Science*; Behe, *Darwin's Black Box*; Gould, *Rocks of Ages*; Overman, *A Case Against Accident and Self-Organization*; Thaxton, C. B., W. L. Bradley, and R. L. Olsen, *The Mystery of Life's Origin* (Dallas: Lewis and Stanley, 1984); Denton, M. *Evolution: A Theory in Crisis* (Bethesda, MD: Adler & Adler, 1986); Johnson, *Darwin on Trial* (Washington, DC: Regnery Gateway, 1991).

NOTES